W9-AUM-269

THE MAN WHO WOULDN'T GIVE UP

HENRY CLAY

BORN: APRIL 12, 1777

DIED: JUNE 29, 1852

Three times candidate for the presidency of the United States, Henry Clay never let his personal ambition override his firm belief in the ideals of sound government and the preservation of the freedoms insured by the Constitution. His famous words, "I'd rather be right than be President," are the key to a driving personality whose long range views saved the Union in three dramatic crises, and earned him prominence as The Great Compromiser.

Books by Katharine E. Wilkie

JOHN SEVIER
Son of Tennessee

THE MAN WHO WOULDN'T GIVE UP
Henry Clay

THE MAN WHO WOULDN'T GIVE UP

HENRY CLAY

by Katharine E. Wilkie

Julian Messner, Inc.   New York

Published by Julian Messner, Inc.
8 West 40 Street, New York 18

Published simultaneously in Canada
by The Copp Clark Publishing Co. Limited

© Copyright 1961 by Katharine E. Wilkie

FIFTH PRINTING, 1962

Printed in the United States of America
Library of Congress Catalog Card No. 61-6370

TO ISABEL

CONTENTS

1

A COUNTRY BOY COMES TO TOWN

HENRY CLAY AND HIS STEPFATHER, CAPTAIN HAL WATKINS, reined in their horses and sat looking down the hill at the sprawling town of Richmond. In spite of the fact that it numbered some five hundred dwellings and business places, it seemed a metropolis to the fourteen-year-old boy. He had lived all his young life at Clay's Spring, the family farm only a few miles from Hanover Court House. Hanover Court House was a small country hamlet quite different from the flourishing town which he and his stepfather were approaching. Except for a few wealthy landowners, the farmers in Hanover County, Virginia, were poor country people. Now as the man and the boy rode toward Richmond, Henry watched wide-eyed as numerous carriages drawn by spirited horses rolled along the streets of the town in the valley below.

"I guess Richmond is a right big place," the boy ventured, looking straight ahead.

The man glanced quickly in his direction. "You may still go to Kentucky with us, Henry. It isn't too late. You know you don't have to stay in Virginia."

Henry shook his head. "I made up my mind a long time ago, Captain Hal. I want to stay in Virginia. Nothing is going to stop me from becoming a lawyer."

The captain gave an exasperated sigh. "It may be some time before Mr. Tinsley can take you in his office. Even though he serves as Clerk of the Chancery Court, he can use

9

only a certain number of copyists, and working for him will not mean that you are studying law. Merely copying legal documents and court records does not guarantee that you will ever rise higher."

"It is a step in the right direction," Henry returned quietly. "I shall be in contact with lawyers and courts and legal proceedings. I can wait. In the meantime I shall work hard for your friend Mr. Denny, who has promised to employ me in his general store."

Captain Watkins gave a shrug. He had discovered a long time ago that it was useless to argue with Henry. The boy was lighthearted, sunny and gay, but he could be stubborn on occasions. When he chose a goal, near at hand or far away, he did not stop until he reached it.

The two riders made their way down the hill into Richmond. As the traffic of the town became heavier, Henry's keen eyes missed nothing. They noted a steady stream of wagons and drays that followed the main road along the James River. This was the commercial section of the town. When the travelers looked upward, they spied the handsome homes overlooking the business area. For the most part, the best residential sections were built on the hills.

With beating heart Henry recognized in the distance an imposing white-columned building that must be the Statehouse. There his heroes—Patrick Henry, Thomas Jefferson and other well-known though lesser men—made their speeches. That was where Henry Clay of Hanover County would one day rise to address an audience.

"Henry!"

The dreaming boy gave a guilty start. His stepfather was frowning.

"I called you twice. Wake up, lad. We are at Mr. Denny's store."

They tied their horses at the hitching rail and went inside the long, rambling frame building. Henry looked about with little enthusiasm at the piles of boxes and barrels and stacks of merchandise.

A middle-aged man came forward to meet them. He held out a hand in welcome. "I have been expecting you all day," he said cordially to Captain Watkins. "Come into my office, where we may talk without interruption."

He led the way to a small room at the rear of the store. There he pulled out chairs for his visitors and sat down in one himself. His eyes swept Henry up and down.

"So this is the young man of whom you told me," he said.

Captain Watkins nodded. "My stepson. He does not want to set out for Kentucky with us when we leave next month. I am happy that he will be in your hands, for he will have no near relatives in Virginia except his brother George, who is my eldest stepson. According to the laws of the state, George inherited the family plantation. A poor parcel of land it is, but he refuses to leave it."

Mr. Denny seemed hardly to have heard the Captain's words. He stared at Henry until the boy felt almost uncomfortable. Now the storekeeper was peering over his spectacles.

"I shall expect you to rise early, retire early and work hard during the hours between. Follow that pattern and you may be a partner in the business someday."

Henry shook his head. "I plan to be a lawyer, sir," he replied courteously.

Mr. Denny scowled. "I thought you wanted to enter the mercantile world."

Captain Watkins spoke up quickly. "It is true that at the present moment he thinks he wishes to become a lawyer. It may be only a passing fancy. He is too young to realize that the legal road is long and arduous. Frankly, he has neither money nor influence. He is only fourteen, Mr. Denny. He will probably change his mind many times before he is a man."

Henry said nothing, but he knew that his stepfather was wrong. With honest eyes he looked at the merchant. "I intend to be a lawyer as fast as the way opens up, Mr. Denny. In the meantime, I must make a living. I shall try to be as good a clerk as possible as long as I work for you. Is that satisfactory, sir?"

Mr. Denny looked hard at Henry. Apparently he liked what he saw. "Fair enough, young man. You may discover that you like storekeeping better than you think. Let us shake hands upon the deal."

Henry accepted the proffered hand, but there was a gleam of skepticism in his thoughtful blue eyes. Why did everyone try to discourage him? He knew what he wanted— and he intended to get it.

Because he had grown up under his mother's watchful care, Henry gave value for value received during the months that followed. There was no more faithful clerk in the entire store than Henry, but when closing time came each day the boy always noted it with a thankful heart. The ceaseless loading and unloading of boxes, barrels and bundles in the warehouse, the displaying of merchandise and the ringing of money upon the counter had small appeal to him.

The days and weeks came and went. Henry returned home for a few days to see the family off to Kentucky. It gave him a strange feeling to watch the wagons being loaded with the familiar household furnishings which had been a part of his childhood. It was as though his roots were being torn up, never to be restored.

His mother led him aside for a few words of farewell before the cavalcade started. There was a lump in her son's throat as he looked down at the plump, energetic little woman he had too often taken for granted. He knew that he would miss her more than he could tell her in words.

As usual, Elizabeth Clay Watkins came straight to the point. There had been no time in her busy life for dilly-dallying.

"I wish you were going to Kentucky with us, Henry. However, you are remaining in Virginia by your own choice."

Henry nodded. All that had been discussed many times before.

"You are only fourteen, but you have always seemed old for your years. If you need advice, come to George—although you have as steady a head on your shoulders as he has. I wish I had the means to send you to the College of William and Mary at Williamsburg, but I haven't. I believe with all my heart that if you don't allow yourself to become discouraged you will find a way to become a lawyer someday."

"That I shall!" Henry declared, his eyes flashing.

"I hope you will come out to Kentucky after that. I have heard they need lawyers there, but I think you are wise to remain in Virginia now. On the frontier where we are going you would not have the opportunities that will arise in Richmond. Never forget that your father was an honored and respected Baptist preacher. Be careful of your associates. A man is known by the company he keeps."

Henry stood for a long time looking after the procession as it wound out of sight. The house would seem very empty without the shouts and voices of the young Clays and the little Watkinses. He turned to George, who stood beside him.

"I guess I'm a man now. I'm completely on my own."

George threw a brotherly arm about his shoulders. "Don't forget to come back to the farm whenever you can. The old Pamunkey River will always be waiting. We can dive for the cannon which the British soldiers threw in there during Revolutionary days just as we used to do when we were small boys."

Strangely enough, when Henry went back to Richmond, he was not lonely. Every moment of the day was filled with work at Denny's store. In the evening after a meager supper, as long as there was any light, he lay on his narrow bed in the little room under the sloping eaves at his boarding-house and tried to fortify himself in the principles of grammar and spelling. He knew he would need both in the future. From his tiny window he could see the Capitol. Its tall pillars and classical lines became a lodestar that beckoned him to join the silver-throated and golden-tongued throng of statesmen who gathered there.

At times there seemed no end to his drudgery. He measured yards and yards of silks and muslins for the fine ladies of Richmond. He sold imported books, fine wines and expensive clothing to gentlemen. He watched cargoes of furs, hides and roots come in from the West and depart for the East. Sometimes he was so weary that he would go supperless to his room, throw himself across the bed and fall into a dreamless stupor. Whenever he could snatch a few hours from work he would steal off to the Statehouse to hear James Monroe declaim or John Marshall expound. More than once he caught sight of Thomas Jefferson, and on one occasion he saw President Washington himself on a hurried journey from Philadelphia to Mount Vernon.

At last after nearly a year the long-awaited summons from the Chancery Office came. Henry went at once to look for Mr. Denny. He found him at his desk in his office.

The boy fingered Mr. Tinsley's letter nervously as he broke the news to his employer. "There is a vacancy at the Chancery Office, sir," he said. "I would like to report there tomorrow if it is agreeable to you."

Mr. Denny gave him a long look. "You still wish to be a lawyer?"

"Oh, yes, sir!"

"Then I suppose you must go," the merchant agreed reluctantly. "You have been a good clerk, my boy. I wish you luck."

Henry was very excited next morning as he dressed. When he had gone to the farm on the Sunday before, black Aunt Cindy had starched his linens until they could have stood alone. In her zeal she had done the same to his only suit of "figinny," a Virginia homespun, and the results were startling.

Henry surveyed himself anxiously in the cracked mirror on his wall. The tails of his waistcoat seemed to stand straight out.

"One could play at draughts on it," he muttered, craning his neck to get a better glimpse. "Oh, botheration! Patrick Henry did not have his clothes tailored in London. Mine will have to do."

It was a dark November day when he set out at a brisk pace for the Capitol. By now he had completely forgotten his countrified appearance. After a hasty breakfast his spirits were soaring as though it were mid-June. At last he was setting out on his chosen road.

Inside the Statehouse he went hurriedly down the main hall, not even stopping to admire the statue of Washington by the sculptor Houdon. He had seen it many times already, and this morning his mind was not on statuary. It was on Henry Clay!

He ran down the stairs at the end of the hall and came to the door of the Chancery Office. With beating heart he opened it and stepped across the threshold. A number of young men were writing away behind high desks. It seemed to Henry that each of them stopped his work and turned in the newcomer's direction. His face reddened, and he smoothed his pale-gold hair nervously.

The gentleman who was directing the copyists stepped forward. If he noticed anything different about Henry's attire, he made no sign, but some of the clerks were not so tactful. The boy from Hanover County was quite certain he saw amused glances here and there.

"You must be Henry Clay," the gentleman said kindly. "I am Mr. Tinsley. Welcome to our midst, sir. These are your fellow workers. Now let me see a sample of your penmanship."

Henry took the quill that Peter Tinsley held out to him. He dipped it into an inkwell and wrote several lines upon a sheet of foolscap. Mr. Tinsley examined it carefully.

"Good!" he commented. "Your handwriting is clear, legible and firm. It shows character, Mr. Clay."

"Thank you, sir," Henry replied. His confidence was returning in spite of the close scrutiny he was undergoing from the young men about him.

"Here is your desk," Mr. Tinsley told him. "You will begin your duties by copying this deed."

Henry went straight to work. Occasionally he glanced out of the corner of his eye at his companions, but they all worked diligently until the tall clock in the corner struck the hour of noon.

Mr. Tinsley rose from his desk as though he were in some mysterious way connected with the timepiece. "My clerks eat at the coffeehouse across the street," he told Henry. "I am turning you over to Mr. Wilson, the senior clerk."

A noisy, carefree group made their way down the steps of the Statehouse and across the street where their noonday meal was waiting. Most of the young men were friendly, and Henry felt that he would be happy among them.

One, however, was an overbearing bully. He looked superciliously at Henry. "I say, would you tell me something, young Clay," he drawled.

Henry nodded. Something told him to be on his guard.

"Who is your tailor?" the other asked sneeringly.

Henry drew himself up to his full height and surveyed the speaker unsmilingly. A dead silence prevailed among the young men about the table.

"Where I come from, sir, we have a saying: 'Clothes do not make the man.' I am aware that my clothes have an awkward air, but I cannot yet afford others. Until such time as I can, I shall wear these with dignity," Henry informed him icily.

"Hurrah!"

"Bully for you, Clay!"

"That's paying him in his own coin!"

Their excited voices were punctuated by a round of applause. Henry smiled. These were decent fellows in spite

the rest of the day Henry moved about in a daze. Would he ever be able to move audiences to tears and laughter and admiration as Patrick Henry moved them? Did he dare even to hope?

The months went by on wings. Occasionally Henry returned to the farm to see George. Now and then a letter came from Kentucky, but the mail was irregular, for the postriders must cross many miles of rough wild country often infested by white renegades and unfriendly Indians. Whenever the letters came, Henry felt a momentary pang of homesickness for his family, but it never lasted long. They seemed in another world, and he was living here and now.

By this time the young man from Hanover County had become a part of Richmond, and Richmond a part of him. The older clerks had moved out into the fields of law and commerce and made room for the younger boys. Henry was acknowledged to be the best copyist in the office. Still he felt dissatisfied and unfulfilled.

"Where will this lead me?" he asked. "I want to become a lawyer. But how?"

"You should have chosen wealthy parents," Will Sharp told him. "Then you could have attended the College of William and Mary. Or you might have had influential contacts and studied under some prominent lawyer."

Henry set his wide mouth in a stubborn line. "Neither door is open to me. Nevertheless, I shall be a lawyer. Wait and see."

In spite of his restlessness Henry was far from unhappy. He made the most of his free time. Along with his companions he worshiped the great legal figures from afar. Together with his co-workers he patterned his dress, his actions, his very thoughts on those of Mr. Marshall, Mr. Monroe, Mr. Jefferson and Mr. Randolph. Like all young Virginians of his day he spent his leisure hours in conversation, drinking and card playing. Among all the clerks in

Mr. Tinsley's office the gayest, the loudest and the most popular one was young Mr. Clay of Hanover County. But in spite of his conviviality, he never missed a way at work or an opportunity to visit the Assembly when it was in session.

2

HENRY GETS HIS CHANCE

A FLUTTER OF EXCITEMENT RAN OVER THE CHANCERY Office. All the copyists and clerks pretended to be hard at work, but they were keenly aware of the small, stooped, bald-headed old man in clothes that had been fashionable during the Revolution. The old gentleman was talking earnestly with Mr. Tinsley.

"He looks as though he had stepped out of a book," Henry whispered to Will Sharp.

"In a way he has—the Book of the Past," Will answered. He looked across the room to make sure that Mr. Tinsley's eyes were not on him. "Don't you know who he is?" he finished.

Henry shook his head.

"That is Judge Wythe, Chief Justice of the High Court of Chancery."

Henry surveyed the visitor with fresh interest. Everyone had heard of Judge Wythe.

"He signed the Declaration of Independence in '76," Will continued, speaking out of the corner of his mouth. "He helped to write the Constitution of the United States. With Thomas Jefferson and Edmund Pendleton's help, he revised the laws of Virginia to fit the Commonwealth instead of the Crown."

"That's not all," whispered Henry's neighbor on the other side. "He's a confirmed old bachelor. At least, each of his two wives died so long ago that everyone thinks of him as

21

a bachelor. They say he bathes in cold water straight from the well each morning. Br-r-r!"

Mr. Tinsley and his visitor looked in the direction of the young men. Fearing that their companion's spirited account of Judge Wythe's morning ablutions had reached their elders' ears, Henry and Will applied themselves zealously to their work.

Presently Mr. Tinsley held up a sheet of foolscap covered with copperplate characters written in a flowing hand. The old gentleman beside him looked intently at the copyists.

"Whose work is this?" Mr. Tinsley asked.

The youths looked at the paper. Their eyes turned toward Henry. He blushed and stepped forward.

"It is mine, sir."

The Judge's keen eyes swept him from head to foot. Henry felt as though they were boring a hole straight through him. At last the old gentleman spoke.

"I am Chancellor Wythe," he said, stretching out a gnarled and twisted right hand. "The infirmities of age force me to seek a secretary. Do you think you would like the position?"

Henry's heart leaped. Here was the opportunity for which he had been hoping. He would be closely associated with the man whom many considered the foremost lawyer in the United States. In the boy's mind a rosy path to fame and fortune opened up before him.

"Yes, sir, I would," Henry replied. "Indeed, I would."

Judge Wythe's faded old eyes twinkled. "I warn you I am a hard taskmaster. I am cross and crotchety, and I have all the whims of old age. Do you still want the job?"

Henry's eyes twinkled in reply. For a fleeting second he felt himself on an equal footing with the Chancellor. Boy though Henry was, he sensed the old man's need for a companion as well as an amanuensis.

"Yes, sir," he answered without hesitation.

The old man seemed pleased. "Very well. I am employing you. You will report to my home on Shockoe Hill in the morning. You will eat your noon meal with me, but you will keep your present lodgings."

Shockoe Hill was the fashionable section of Richmond where the leading families of the city lived. Henry had often strolled there in the evening and looked through the windows of the brightly lighted houses. He had watched the fine carriages deposit their richly dressed guests at the broad front doors for a ball, a reception or a musicale. The country lad had looked longingly into the interiors with their graceful stairways and glittering chandeliers. He had listened to snatches of gay conversation and strains of lilting music. It was a world he longed to enter. Someday he intended to be a part of it.

Early the next day after Judge Wythe's visit to the Chancery Office, Henry lifted the gleaming brass knocker on the door of the Judge's house. He heard its echoes resound within. If he felt some trepidation as a Negro butler in a swallow-tailed black coat ushered him into the study, it vanished a moment later with his host's pleasant welcome. The boy had time for only a glance at the elegant furnishings and richly paneled walls before he found himself at a long table across from Judge Wythe. A pile of fresh white paper and half a dozen pointed goose quills lay before him.

"You will write as I dictate," the Judge told him. "And write with care, Henry Clay. I wish my exact words recorded."

"I will try, sir," Henry answered. His hand shook with excitement as he reached for a pen. "I may take a little while to become accustomed to your manner of speaking."

The old man's eyes softened. "A great many young men over the years have become accustomed to my manner of speaking. John Marshall, who is the acknowledged leader of the Richmond bar. James Monroe, now a United States senator. Thomas Jefferson, our present Secretary of State. I could mention others. They all served under me in one capacity or another."

Henry Clay had a daring thought. Was it possible—no, it could not be—and yet—

He stole a glance toward the speaker. Was the old man implying that he, Henry Clay, might rise to fame along with those others? That was almost too much to hope for. He looked for an answer in the wise, old, wrinkled face, but none was there.

"These are parlous times, boy," the Judge went on. "I have seen the ship of state launched and I have seen it almost founder on the rocks of quarrels, selfishness and misunderstanding. In my opinion, even stormier waters lie ahead. America is a great and daring experiment. We have two kinds of men in our government: those who sincerely believe that all men are created equal and those who do not. The latter call themselves Federalists."

"Surely they believe in the principles of the Declaration of Independence," Henry protested.

The Judge's lip curled. "Remember what that chief Federalist Alexander Hamilton said: 'Your people, sir, is a great *beast.*' These men pretend to believe in democracy. Actually they think that only the wealthy and well-educated are fit to rule. They think a man's worth is governed by the size of his purse. They still yearn for the royal magnificence and pomp which the Revolution should have ended in America. In all ways these Federalists seek to pattern our government after that of Great Britain."

"But that is wrong!" Henry cried passionately. "We fought to make ourselves free. Is freedom only a word?"

"Thomas Jefferson does not think so," the old man answered, smiling. "Of all my students he is the brightest star. You will hear more from him one day regarding the rights—and responsibilities—of the common man. Set your course in his train and do not hesitate to follow it. Someday he may be the greatest man in America."

Henry had become bolder as he listened to the other's frank, free manner of speaking. He leaned forward now, his blue eyes shining.

"But his thoughts are yours, sir. All Virginia is well aware that you have taught such liberal ideas as his for years."

The old man shook his head. "What matter if I helped to light the torch? My course is nearly run, Henry. My day is almost over. But Jefferson's has hardly started. On such as he—and those who follow him—depends the future of America. I am a legal man, a lawyer, a jurist—and a teacher. Of all those titles I think I am proudest of the last; that is, unless you add to it the word Republican. I am a Jeffersonian Republican and proud to bear the name."

The young secretary had almost forgotten the purpose for which he had been summoned to the house on Shockoe Hill. He was beginning a new life. Each day from early till late he would work hard and learn from the great Judge Wythe. The future, Henry could not foresee; but this much he somehow knew. A career in the service of his country lay ahead. The path to the future was bathed in a golden light.

The sound of Judge Wythe's voice brought him back to his surroundings. "Let us set to work," the old man was saying. "There is much to be done. My correspondence has piled up."

The end of the first day found Henry almost exhausted. His employer's speech had been full of words that Henry had never heard. Not only law terms, but words from Greek and Roman classicists, Euripides, Thucydides, Pericles and others. He labored over their writing and guessed at their spelling. The Judge watched his efforts without comment.

When Henry arrived the next morning, Judge Wythe went directly to the bookshelves and pulled down several volumes. He piled them on a chair.

"You may take them home with you tonight. I think you need them," he said.

That night in the attic bedroom at his boardinghouse Henry examined the books carefully. They were Plutarch's *Lives,* a copy of Homer's works, two grammar texts and a history of the world. The young clerk threw himself across the bed and began to read. The print was fine and the light from the single candle was poor. His head ached from his day's labors, and he felt as though hammers were pounding on his temples.

Presently Will Sharp thrust his head in at the bedroom door. His hair was freshly pomaded, and his snowy shirt frill was straight from the hands of the laundress.

"What are you doing?" he demanded. "We are going to Mrs. Gilbert's coffeehouse for a round of loo. Come along, Henry."

Henry shook his head. "I can't spare the time. There's so much I must learn, Will. I shall never be able to satisfy Judge Wythe if I don't make a dent in my ignorance."

Will stared in disbelief. "It is certainly not like you, Henry Clay, to forego an evening of cards and sociability for books and study."

He ran off down the hall. Henry turned back to the grammar book in his hand. The lines swam before his eyes and the words ran together. His mind refused to absorb the author's ideas. After a few futile attempts to recapture the spirit of study, Henry dropped the volume on the floor.

He smoothed back his flaxen hair and thrust a red, white, and blue cockade into the lapel of the new waistcoat he had bought only yesterday with the money Judge Wythe had advanced him. That little rosette, symbol of sympathy for the French Revolution, should tell all who cared to know that he was a true Democratic-Republican. Not for him the black cockade of the pro-British Federalists. He, Henry Clay, was a Jeffersonian Republican in full agreement with the *liberté, égalité, fraternité* of France. As fast as his long legs could carry him he set out to find the lights, laughter and companionship of Mrs. Gilbert's coffeehouse.

Before long Henry had completed the books which his mentor had lent him. With a joyful heart he carried them back to the house on Shockoe Hill. In spite of numerous interruptions he felt that he had finished them in record time.

He anticipated at least a modicum of praise from Judge Wythe.

Instead the old man frowned. He glanced from the books to the young secretary and back again.

"So soon? You must have *skimmed,* young man."

"I read them through," Henry protested.

The Judge shook his head. "But you could not have absorbed them. You must be more thorough. A good foundation is essential. So you plan to study law, Henry?"

The abruptness of the question startled Clay.

"It has long been my dream, sir—if I can find a way."

"I will take you as my pupil." The old man held up a hand to stem Henry's gratitude. "No flowery speeches, please. A long road of application and work—perhaps drudgery—lies ahead of you. I warn you, my young friend, the law is a jealous mistress."

The next few weeks sped by on wings. Henry found his teacher was right in predicting a path of hard work, but he applied himself diligently to his studies. If he did not always dig as deeply as the old man wished, he heard no word of reproof. Actually he labored hard, but intense research was not possible for Henry Clay. He was brilliant, alert and inquiring, but hours of study were foreign to his nature.

A close proximity to Chancellor Wythe brought Henry other advantages in addition to the study of law. As the chancellor's protégé he had entree to doors that otherwise would have been shut. No one would have recognized the courtly, fair-haired young gallant in clothes of the latest mode as the awkward country boy in ill-fitting "figinny" who had made his entrance upon the Richmond scene a few short years ago.

Secretly old George Wythe looked upon his work and rejoiced. There was not the slightest doubt in his mind that Henry would one day attain success just as his other pupils had done.

Four years passed swiftly while the Chancellor's protégé

worked doggedly day after day. Young Henry Clay had a brilliant mind, but he lacked the painstaking habits of a scholar. His path was rough.

One afternoon Judge Wythe closed the book in his hand and looked critically at the young man on the other side of the fireplace.

"You should have some months in a lawyer's office. You need to see a lawyer deal with his clients. You should experience law applied in a rough-and-tumble world. You must learn more about people. Then you will be ready for your bar examinations."

Henry nodded. He had heard a great deal about those examinations.

The old man continued. "I have talked with Attorney General Brooke about you. He says he can use a likely young man in his office. In addition, he will give you board and lodgings in his home."

Henry gasped. He had hardly expected such good fortune to come so soon.

"You have a rare opportunity, my boy. See that you make the best of it."

By now Henry had found his voice. "I shall try my best to do so, sir. But the truly rare opportunity has been my association with you. I shall never forget the hours I have spent in this room."

The old man looked pleased. "See that you don't," he said crustily. "I should like to think that I have made my mark upon you. You are still, I trust, a good Republican."

"As staunch a one as I know how to be," Henry declared.

"You share my convictions about slavery?"

Henry followed the old man's gaze as it fell upon a young Negro servant going down the broad hallway. He was a handsome, intelligent, well-mannered man whom the old man loved almost as a son. Indeed, his enemies said he was his son.

"I have solved my personal problems," Wythe said with a sigh. "As you know, my servants were freed long ago. How they will survive in a hostile world when I am gone I do not know. But the men of your generation must solve the slavery question somehow for the country. If it is not solved properly, it may rend the nation one day."

"I will try," Henry promised humbly. It seemed to him that the Judge was leaving him a large order to fill.

A year in Judge Brooke's palatial home gave an extra polish to Henry's already urbane manners. He became fast friends with Francis Brooke, the Attorney General's younger brother, and with another young man named Tom Ritchie.

With them and other young Virginians he formed a debating society which he enjoyed to the utmost, for he had determined to make his naturally fine voice an asset in his chosen career.

One morning, soon after Henry moved to his new quarters in the Attorney General's mansion, a messenger on horseback drew rein before the front door. He was a countryman who seemed a little in awe of the fine surroundings.

Summoned by the butler, Henry came out to meet the horseman. He reached up for the letter which the rider drew from one of his saddlebags.

"I'm sorry, sir," the messenger said awkwardly. "My wife was ill and I could not leave her when your brother's servant came to my farm. Then for several days the rains made the roads impassable. I came as soon as I could."

With unseeing eyes Henry stared at the missive in his hand. George dead of smallpox at twenty-two! What would become of the farm at Clay's Spring? John was next in the line of inheritance—but John was far away in Kentucky.

The entire family was far away in Kentucky—that is, all but Henry. No close blood tie remained to him in Virginia. As he realized that George was gone forever, he felt that he was indeed a stranger in a strange land. With bowed head he turned and walked into the house.

Although Henry felt his brother's death deeply, he met life with a young man's resilience. The months passed swiftly. In a year's time he presented himself before the bar for his examinations. The ordeal was hard, but Henry had been well-tutored. As soon as he learned that he had been accepted, he set off at full speed for Judge Wythe's house.

He hardly waited to be announced before he rushed into the library. "I've been admitted to the bar!" he sang out triumphantly.

The old man gave a dry chuckle. "So I assumed when I saw you from my window. You were running as though the hounds were at your heels. What do you intend to do now?"

Henry Clay considered for a moment as he stared into the crackling flames on the hearth. "My final family ties with Virginia were broken when my brother George died last year. I suppose I shall soon be off for Kentucky. My mother and my stepfather are expecting me. I haven't seen them for nearly six years. They told me when they left that they would expect me in Kentucky someday."

"Is this a visit or a change of residence?" the Judge asked, eying him keenly.

Henry did not reply immediately. At last he answered slowly. "I shall live there permanently. They say Kentucky is a likely place for young lawyers."

His mentor smiled. "So I have heard. Land grants and claims are so tangled there that only legal minds can straighten them out—and sometimes even they fail. When you go, I shall give you letters of introduction to Virginians who have preceded you. They are old pupils of mine. You may find their friendship useful."

3

KENTUCKY AT LAST

A TRAVELER ON HORSEBACK RODE INTO THE LITTLE BACKWOODS settlement of Versailles, Kentucky, on a December afternoon in 1797. He was a tall, lanky young man whose rumpled clothing bore witness to the fact that he had come on a long journey.

He brought his horse to a standstill in front of a large, rambling log cabin on the main street of the town.

"I'm looking for Captain Watkins' tavern," he told a man who was chewing a straw and leaning indolently against the corner of the building.

"You've found it," the man observed laconically, removing the straw only long enough to utter the words.

Henry Clay dismounted, tied his horse to the hitching post and entered the door of the inn. The common room, as the main dining room was called, was a cheery spot that warmed his heart after the poor accommodations of his journey over the mountains. There was a crackling fire in the huge stone fireplace. In the rear of the room hams hung down from the low beams. The smell of good food pervaded every nook and cranny.

Henry's eyes swept over the dozen or more customers seated at the tables in an effort to find his mother. He soon discovered her directing the movements of several Negro waiters with trays and covered dishes. She looked a little older, a trifle smaller, than when he had seen her last, but she was the same plump, busy, energetic person she had always been.

Her son looked about him. He did not care to have a reunion with strangers looking on, so he slipped quietly through an open door into a hall. A Negro woman with a pile of coverlets in her arms was passing by.

"I should like to see Mrs. Watkins," he told her. The woman turned from him and walked between the tables toward her mistress. Henry watched her say a few words to Elizabeth Watkins, who looked toward the hall. Henry slipped farther back into the shadows.

Presently his mother came hurrying across the room and through the door. Henry stepped out from his corner.

A startled look of recognition swept over her face. "Henry! My little Henry!"

"Your big Henry now, Mother. Not by the wildest stretch of the imagination could anyone call me little Henry any longer."

"Always my little Henry!" she insisted through happy tears.

After the customers had finally taken their departure, the family sat down together around a table loaded with as many of Henry's favorite dishes as his mother could manage in so short a time.

The young lawyer looked up and down the length of the table. It was good to be among one's own again. These brothers and half brothers were his own flesh and blood. Mother was still Mother. And Captain Hal at the head of the table was as dear to him as his own father, whom he remembered through the mist of years. A little heavier and a little grayer, Captain Hal regarded Henry with fatherly pride.

"To think that one of my sons is a lawyer!" Mother exclaimed. "It is a great thing which you have achieved, Henry."

Henry turned his pockets inside out and surveyed them ruefully. "A lawyer, it is true, but a penniless one. I rode to Kentucky with no possessions but the horse beneath me."

His mother and Captain Hal exchanged glances. Then his

stepfather cleared his throat. "There is a small amount still due you from your father's estate, and in addition I can advance you any sum of money within reason, my boy."

Henry shook his head. "I was not hinting for a loan. In fact, I am not quite so poverty-stricken as I may sound. I have a couple of sovereigns in my wallet which should tide me over until I take in a few fees."

"You may stay here as long as you like," his mother told him. "Captain Hal and I are agreed on that. Our home will always be yours."

Her son flashed her a grateful smile. "I know that, Mother. But I think I shall soon make a place for myself. Judge Wythe gave me letters of introduction to John Breckinridge, George Nicholas and James Brown. Those letters should help me get a start."

Captain Hal nodded vigorously. "They certainly should. Mr. Breckinridge and Mr. Nicholas are leading members of the bar at Lexington. Mr. Brown practices at Frankfort, but he and his wife go frequently to Lexington to see her parents, Colonel and Mrs. Thomas Hart."

"All three men studied under Judge Wythe," Henry said. "I only hope I may someday be as successful as they are."

The next week Henry ended his visit at Versailles and rode toward Lexington. The neighboring town lay about ten miles away. The young man felt a pang of homesickness for genteel Richmond as he came to the main street of the town where he had decided to settle. The log and frame houses of Lexington were in decided contrast to the orderly brick buildings of Richmond.

Clay drew in his reins sharply as three men on horseback raced furiously past him. Several bystanders cheered them on. Two middle-aged women in linsey-woolsey gowns and calico bonnets scuttled for shelter into a convenient doorway.

The young Virginian smiled as he watched a well-dressed pedestrian making his way along the hard-packed thoroughfare. With his patrician air he would have graced the streets of Richmond. Behind him two Indians in blankets walked stolidly along without glancing to right or left. Almost beneath Clay's feet a couple of small Negro boys squatted on the ground and rolled dice.

Henry's wave of nostalgia had disappeared. Here was a place where the East and the West, the old and the new, the tried and the untried met and mingled. Suddenly he was seized with a consuming desire to become part and parcel of the town. He imagined that even the air in this sylvan spot was sweeter and fresher than that of the Old Dominion.

The new arrival had already noted several taverns, but he had passed them by. Now he was well into the center of town. Realizing that the hour was late, he pulled his mount to a stop in front of an inn on the corner of Main and Mulberry streets. A sign swaying in the December wind proclaimed that it was Postlethwaite's Tavern.

After Henry had turned his horse over to a groom and secured a room for himself, he made his way to the dining room. He was eager to present his letters, but he knew he must wait until morning. Now he was ready to eat. The long ride from Versailles had quickened his appetite.

To his surprise the viands set before him were well-cooked, succulent and pleasing in appearance. They resembled in no way the heavy, greasy frontier fare that he had experienced on his journey over the mountains from Virginia.

"Amazing, isn't it?" a voice said close by.

Henry looked up quickly. His eyes met those of a handsomely dressed gentleman in his middle thirties who was seated at the next table. From head to foot he was pervaded with a sense of well-being and good humor. Henry felt attracted to him at once.

"It's amazing, isn't it?" the gentleman repeated.

"What's amazing?" Henry demanded.

The man waved one hand at the plate in front of Henry and another at the warm, friendly interior of the tavern with its great stone fireplace and its candles twinkling in their wall sconces. "One would scarcely expect such accommodations west of Philadelphia or New York—or Richmond, Virginia."

"I have just come from Richmond," Henry said. "Perhaps you will be so kind as to direct me to some gentlemen to whom I bear letters."

"While I do not reside in Lexintgon, I think I know everyone here," the stranger returned. "To whom are your letters addressed?"

"To Mr. John Breckinridge, Mr. George Nicholas and Mr. James Brown," Henry told him.

A look of surprise came over the other's face. As Henry concluded, the man broke into a hearty laugh.

"I am James Brown," he said. "The other gentlemen you mention are fellow lawyers and friends of mine. May I ask your name, sir?"

"Henry Clay, recently of Richmond. I read law under Judge Wythe."

Brown signaled a nearby waiter. "Move my things to Mr. Clay's table. He and I will finish our meal together."

A few minutes later the two were chatting away like old friends. Henry could scarcely believe his good fortune. His life in Kentucky was having an auspicious beginning.

"Any friend of the Chancellor is a friend of mine," James Brown declared. "I am sure Mr. Nicholas and Mr. Breckinridge will say the same. I shall introduce you to them tomorrow. As you probably know already, George Nicholas is professor of law and politics at our local institution of higher learning, Transylvania College. He is well-fitted to hold the position for, in addition to being a leading lawyer, he was a member of the constitutional convention in our state and the first attorney general under Governor Isaac Shelby."

Henry drew a deep breath. "He sounds interesting. How about Mr. Breckinridge?"

"Now there's a man for you!" his informant exclaimed enthusiastically. "Tall, handsome, brilliant—a gentleman by birth and connections. He succeeded Nicholas as attorney general of Kentucky. At present he is a member from Fayette County (of which Lexington is the seat) in the House of Representatives at Frankfort. Of course he will go on to the national capital someday. He is too big a man to be confined to state politics. I tell you he is a real Democratic-Republican. None of these despicable Federalist tendencies for him. He is a true advocate of freedom and the rights of man. He knows that France, not England, is our friend abroad. After all, the French Revolution came about because certain Frenchmen dared to believe that the common man can govern himself, and that kings and a privileged class have no divine rights. Oh, pshaw! My wife Nancy would say that I am making a speech as usual."

Henry Clay sat enthralled. He hardly dared to breathe as his companion went on to paint pictures of men who hitherto had been only names to him. Now he grew bolder.

"And James Brown—what of him?"

The older man laughed. "Oh, you will get to know him better as time goes by. He's not such a bad fellow." He pulled a heavy gold watch from his waistcoat pocket. "I'll tell you what I'll do, Clay. I'll take you with me to a meeting of our Junto. The gentlemen we have been discussing will probably be there. So will the young bloods like John Allen, Jesse Bledsoe and George Bibb, who will be your rivals in the legal field. It will be a rare opportunity for you to become acquainted with Lexington's lawyers. I shall put you up for membership if you like. It's only a formality. We are a democratic group and welcome all newcomers. Come along. We are already late."

By this time they were striding down the darkened streets that were lighted only by an occasional gleam from a house or shop.

"I belonged to a Democratic club in Richmond," Henry Clay said. "We met to debate the insults of Britain, the perfidy of John Jay, Minister to England, and the glories of the French Revolution—"

"You will feel at home tonight," James Brown told him

grimly. "We Kentuckians don't like the Federalists either. There's no more time to talk. Here we are."

Henry found himself presently in a long, smoke-filled room where a score or more of young lawyers and a few middle-aged ones were gathered to discuss the influence of the French Revolution. The subject of the debate for the evening was: Resolved that a second war with England is inevitable.

Seated beside Brown, Henry followed eagerly the arguments presented by several speakers; to his surprise, however, the debate was over before he felt the subject was exhausted.

"Surely they will not stop now," he whispered to James Brown. "Much more remains to be said."

James Brown gave him a long, speculative look. "You think so?" He pushed back his chair and rose to his feet. "Gentlemen, my friend Henry Clay of Virginia has more to say on the subject just debated. He does not think the discussion is finished. Before he speaks, may I present him to you as a new member for your consideration? I may add that he has read law under Judge Wythe."

All in the space of a few minutes Henry was discussed, cheered and voted a member of the Lexington Junto. In less time than that he was given the floor. Presently he found himself looking down at his audience.

The move had taken him by surprise. He had not expected it. For a moment his customary self-reliance deserted him. Then he raised his head proudly. He knew what he believed. He was not ashamed to declare it.

For a moment he imagined himself back in the Richmond courtroom. "Gentlemen of the jury—" he began.

A ripple of amusement swept over the room. There was a burst of delighted laughter. The young Kentuckians could not believe their ears. Either the newcomer was absent-minded or he was dealing in delightful humor.

Instantly Henry realized his mistake. His face grew hot. Then he threw his shoulders back and plunged into his theme.

"Gentlemen of the jury! I am on trial before you for I am new and unknown—"

For more than an hour he presented to them the theme in which his preceptor Judge Wythe had grounded him so well. From the depths of his heart he spoke of Thomas Jefferson and the rights of man. He dismissed contemptuously the efforts of Spain to woo Kentucky from the Union. With equal abhorrence he spoke of John Jay, who had sided with the British against his own countrymen in the West when he accepted a treaty which took away their trading rights on the Mississippi. Many actions such as Jay's would sweep the country into another war.

At the end of his speech he left no doubts where his sympathies lay. He ended with a clarion call to the banner of Thomas Jefferson. The room rang with the wild applause and the approving shouts of his Republican compatriots. In one bold move Henry Clay had entrenched himself in Kentucky hearts. By the next day the account of the night's events would be all over the streets of Lexington.

His second speech in Lexington took place under somewhat different circumstances. A few days after the Junto episode Mr. Breckinridge, to whom by now he had presented his letter of introduction, sent him to a small backwoods hamlet south of Lexington to collect a bad debt. When he arrived at his journey's end, he found all the men of the village gathered at the blacksmith shop. A political meeting was in session to discuss the candidates for the office of sheriff. Voices were loud and tempers hot. The man for whom Clay was looking was the most bellicose of all.

The rough, unshaven natives regarded the trim young stranger with suspicion. One dark-browed individual set down the stone jug which was passing from hand to hand and shouted, "Speech! Speech!"

Henry found himself pushed by ungentle hands to the center of the crude shed. The smell of perspiration and unwashed bodies sickened him, but his face betrayed no sign of his disgust. He stepped up on the anvil a few feet above the men and surveyed them quietly. Then he plunged into the business at hand.

"My friends, you are about to choose a man for the important office of sheriff," he said in cultured tones that contrasted sharply with the rough accents of the men about him. "I wonder who would have been the choice of that great pioneer Daniel Boone, who lived not so many years ago a few miles from here. It would have been a fearless man—as this man is fearless." Clay pointed a long finger at a bearded giant directly beneath him. The man's chest expanded several inches, and he glanced proudly from side to side at his companions. From that moment he was Clay's slave.

The young lawyer spoke for nearly an hour on Daniel Boone, the hero of the community. His keen eyes observed every change of countenance, every shade of emotion. As the moments passed, his confidence increased. He sensed correctly that he had captivated his audience. At the end of his speech the men applauded wildly.

"Here's your money!" cried the fellow from whom he had been sent to collect the debt. "By heaven, it was worth it to hear a speech like that."

Well satisfied, Henry rode back to Lexington. When John Breckinridge heard the account of the journey he laughed until the tears ran down his cheeks.

"You will do well, young man," he said. "I confess I had my doubts when I first met you. To be sure, you would grace a drawing room, but I wondered if you had the stamina for backwoods living. You have proved today that you can deal with rough men as well as refined ones. And your Republican politics are right. In other words, you are a Kentuckian."

For a time all went well for Henry Clay. There was plenty of business for young lawyers, even for a young Virginia lawyer who had not yet been admitted to the Kentucky bar, when he counted Breckinridge, Nicholas and Brown among his friends. For several months the young man widened his circle of acquaintances and made himself familiar with Kentucky law. On March 20, 1798, he presented his certificate from Virginia and became a full-fledged member of the Kentucky bar.

He did not know it, but he was about to become a Kentucky lawyer in deed as well as in name. Storm clouds lay ahead. Many Kentuckians were of the opinion that the constitution, adopted in 1792 when Kentucky became a state, needed several changes. One group, in particular, disapproved of the clause that forbade the legislature from passing a law to abolish slavery.

"That is not true to Jeffersonian ideals!" Henry cried out on a street corner to a friend. "Even if the majority of voters should desire to do away with slavery, they cannot do it. Either we live in a democracy or we don't."

His companion glanced about cautiously to see if anyone had heard Henry's outburst. "You will do well to keep such thoughts to yourself," he advised. "The wealthy, influential men in this town think differently. When the election comes in May, they will vote against changing the constitution, especially the slavery law."

"Then I will side with the poor, unimportant men," Henry Clay declared.

He threw himself into the quarrel with a zeal of which his old teacher George Wythe would have approved. With all the assurance of youth, Henry was positive he was right. He believed that the thirty thousand slaves in Kentucky must be freed gradually, but they must be freed. His views were the views of Jefferson and Wythe.

The Emancipationists, as men like Clay termed themselves all over the country, believed that all Negroes born after a certain time should be free. While they were children, they would remain with their parents. Then, having been taught a trade, they would be given tools and firearms and sent back to Africa. In the course of time, slavery in America would cease to exist.

However, Emancipation, if it became a law, would lighten the purses of all slaveholders. In Lexington all men who advocated it were regarded as crackpot reformers. John Breckinridge, under the pseudonym A Friend to Order, published a letter in the pages of a Lexington newspaper, the Kentucky *Gazette*. It read:

Are you a large land holder? I suspect not. . . . Are you a slave holder? No, I will give you my right hand if you are. This is the canker that preys upon you. This is what produces all your bellowings about Conventions, Conventions. This is what stirs up your envy, wounds your pride, and makes you cry out at *aristocracy*.

Henry grew hot and cold as he read these words. In all the impetuousness of his twenty-one years he sat down and dashed off a reply:

Can any humane man be happy and contented when he sees near thirty thousand of his fellow beings around him deprived of all the rights which make life desirable, transferred like cattle from the possession of one to another; when he sees the trembling slave under the hammer surrounded by a number of eager purchasers, and feeling all the emotions which arise when one is uncertain into whose tyrannic hands he must next fall; when he beholds the anguish and hears the piercing cries of husbands separated from wives, and children from parents; when, in a word, all the tender and endearing cries of nature are broken asunder and disregarded; and when he reflects that no gradual mode of emancipation is adopted either for these slaves or their posterity. . . .

All America acknowledges the existence of slavery to be an evil. If it be this enormous evil, the sooner we attempt its destruction the better. . . . The first dawn of disease is the moment for remedy. The longer it continues, the more difficult is the cure. . . . Fellow citizens, the present is the moment for coming forward—it is impossible to foresee the consequences of inactivity.

With a bold flourish Henry signed the pseudonym *Scaevola*. He folded the sheet of paper twice and sprang to his feet. There was no time to lose. He would take it at once in person to the office of the Kentucky *Gazette*.

4

SPRING IN KENTUCKY

THE *Scaevola* LETTER CAUSED CONSIDERABLE COMMENT. George Nicholas and John Breckinridge condemned it openly. Once Henry Clay heard Mr. Breckinridge discussing it with some other lawyers gathered about him on Cheapside, the street with the Old World name that ran along the west side of the courthouse.

"That letter doesn't amount to an iota," Breckinridge said contemptuously. "No doubt it is the work of some impractical dreamer without a cent to his name. One of those addlepated fellows who is always wanting to take from the rich and give to the poor."

"He is correct on at least two counts," Henry Clay told himself. "My taxable property is the horse on which I rode over the mountains. Of course I've managed to save some of my fees since then. Someday I mean to be a man of property. And if it's addlepated to believe in equality for all men and freedom for black and white alike, then I'm addlepated."

Inevitably the original constitution was replaced by another one. When the heat of battle between the "Common People" and the "Aristocrats," as the opposing groups styled each other, cooled off, a new constitution had been formed. It provided that the senators and governor should be elected by the voters. The electoral college was a thing of the past. The office of lieutenant-governor (comparable to the national vice-president) was created. But the slavery section remained virtually unchanged. The fight had been fierce.

Preachers thundered from their pulpits; liberals inveighed against the practice, Henry Clay bit his lip in chagrin, but the landed gentry, who were the large slaveholders, decreed that slavery must stay. The second constitution became law on June 1, 1800.

But long before that date Henry Clay found life crowding in upon him to such an extent that matters other than slavery engaged his attention.

All through the bitter political campaign James Brown, who had sided with the landholders (probably because he was one of them), remained his staunch friend.

"I'm a Jeffersonian Republican just as you are, Henry," he told him one afternoon as they stood before Megowan's Tavern, where the young Virginian had taken less expensive lodgings. "Theoretically I believe in the rights of man and the sacredness of the individual, but we are caught in the throes of a powerful system. Practically speaking, the black man is a commodity that is necessary to the prevailing economy. To put it bluntly, the South must have slaves in order to produce cotton. As long as that remains true, Negroes will be sold on the auction block."

Henry Clay shuddered. "That is double talk, James. If one doesn't live up to his ideals, it is better not to have them."

James Brown sighed. "You are very young, Henry, or you would not hold such an opinion." He caught a glimpse of "King Solomon," the white town vagrant, shambling down the street as he pushed a wobbly handcart. "Is a black man worse off than that fellow yonder? Take my man Ham, for instance. He is devoted to me. He and his family have the best of care. They eat well; they live in a comfortable little house; they are cared for when they are ill; they have no debts, no cares, no responsibilities. I doubt whether Ham would accept his freedom if I gave it to him."

"But Ham is a slave," Henry exclaimed with feeling. "He cannot call his soul his own. You could sell him tomorrow and separate him from his family if you chose."

"But I don't choose," Brown returned mildly. "For one cruel master there are twenty good ones. Don't be a Don Quixote tilting at windmills. You need to get your feet on the ground and forget your idealism. You are a personable young man. You should go out in society more. Lexington has many charming members of the fair sex, my lad. You are of marriageable age, you know. You had better develop the practical side of your nature."

He interrupted his remarks long enough to bow to the occupants of a passing carriage. Henry followed the direction of his friend's eyes and then stood staring after the departing vehicle.

His face was aglow as he turned back to the older man. "Now there were two of the loveliest ladies I have seen since I arrived in Kentucky. The younger one, especially, had charm, vivacity—*élan,* I think the French call it—such as I have observed in few of her sex. There went a girl I should like to know, James."

There was evident amusement in the other's eyes. "Now, oddly enough, I prefer the older one. However, if you care to meet her companion, I think it could be arranged. Those two ladies in the carriage were my wife and Lucretia Hart, her younger sister."

When Henry Clay first proclaimed himself a member of the antislavery party, Breckinridge and Nicholas had treated him coolly, but as the weeks went by their feelings subsided. The young man was able, eager—and adaptable. As it become evident that the adoption of a new constitution was practically certain, Henry determined to keep his convictions about slavery to himself. That is, until such time as their expression might bear fruit. He was too intelligent to fan the flames if the fire would do no good. He could wait.

Other matters were filling his mind. Tonight he was preparing to make his first call upon Miss Lucretia Hart. James Brown and his wife were staying at the Hart home for the weekend. Brown had asked Henry to join them for dinner.

"Now you will meet the object of your dreams," he told Henry. "The Hart household is a delightful place. You will find Colonel Hart a most cordial host. He welcomes company, young and old. As you probably know, he is one of the influential men of Lexington. He and his brother Nathaniel were partners with Colonel Richard Henderson in the ill-fated Transylvania venture, when a party of wealthy businessmen attempted to buy almost the whole of Kentucky from the Cherokee Indians just before the Revolution. He owns huge mercantile holdings, a smithy and even a rope-walk, where raw hemp is made into rope for export to the East and also to foreign markets. He is a man of means as well as quite a person in his own right. I'm sure you will like him."

Henry made no reply. He hardly heard James Brown, for his mind held no room for thoughts of jovial, heavy-jowled Colonel Hart. Instead the young man's head was filled with visions of the girl in the violet-colored silk gown whom he had seen for the first time only a few days ago. It was a new experience for Elizabeth Watkins' son. Heretofore he had paid court to half a dozen Richmond belles at a time, romped with them through quadrilles, paid them pretty compliments and promptly forgot them next day when he became engrossed in the business of the courts.

But this was different. All morning the bewitching figure of Lucretia Hart had interposed itself between him and the legal papers on his desk. He had stopped work at an earlier hour than usual and returned to his lodgings. There he had thrown himself upon his bed and lain full length with his hands under his head while he gave himself over to a contemplation of the evening before him.

Now with rapidly beating heart he mounted the steps of the Hart residence on North Mill Street. Presently he lifted the massive knocker on the front door and let it fall. A moment later he was admitted by a black-coated butler.

"I am Mr. Henry Clay," the young man said.

The Negro took his hat and cane. He walked a few steps

ahead of Henry to the archway of the drawing room on the right.

"Mr. Henry Clay," he announced.

Henry's observant eyes took in at a glance the family group in their quietly elegant surroundings. There was ruddy-faced Colonel Hart, whom he knew already by sight. The middle-aged lady in green satin must be his wife. James Brown and his Nancy sat side by side on the French sofa, a picture of connubial bliss. And seated apart on a black mohair hassock—for all the world like a princess, Henry fondly fancied—was Lucretia Hart.

James Brown sprang to his feet as Henry was announced. "Welcome to our midst, my dear Henry," he exclaimed. "Father and Mother Hart, may I present my friend Henry Clay. And to you, Nancy, and you, Lucretia."

After acknowledging the introduction to his host and his wife, Henry Clay bowed in turn to each of the two younger ladies. They surveyed him with interest.

Colonel Hart shook his hand vigorously. The old gentleman was all affability and graciousness.

"Your fame has preceded you, Mr. Clay," he told him. "My son-in-law says you are one of the rising young lawyers of Lexington."

Henry's eyes gleamed with humor. "I fear I have a long distance to travel, but I find the journey exceedingly pleasant, sir."

His eyes sought Lucretia's so directly that the girl blushed and turned away. With an effort, Henry turned aside and devoted his attention to his host's wife and elder daughter.

Although Henry was completely unaware of the fact, Colonel Hart's youngest daughter was noting with absorbed interest the tall, fair-haired young man in impeccably cut clothes with the distinctly different air. It was not his pale-gold hair cut in Directoire fashion or his snowy stock and pointed collar extending almost to his well-molded chin. Nor was it his too-wide mouth and keen blue eyes that seemed to see straight through one. She was not sure just what set him apart. She was merely certain that he was different from other young men.

As for Henry, he was swimming in a delicious haze that was permeated by the graceful form of the young woman to whom he had just been introduced. He knew vaguely that there were others present, but Lucretia—divine name!—was all that mattered. With thirsty eyes, the youthful lawyer drank in her fine delicate features framed in a glory of auburn hair that fell in a cluster of curls on her neck.

"Mr. Henry Clay," she repeated softly.

Henry was still in an ecstasy at hearing his name on her lips when the manservant announced dinner. The Colonel offered his arm to his wife, and Nancy Brown slipped a hand into her husband's.

"Will you take my little Marylander in to dinner, Mr. Clay?" the Colonel asked. He gave Lucretia an affectionate glance as he spoke over his shoulder to Henry. "I call her my little Marylander because she is my last tie with the state where I lived before coming here."

By the time the meal was over, Henry felt that he had known the Harts always. When the party returned to the drawing room, he seated himself beside Lucretia and glanced boldly toward the rosewood spinet inlaid with mother-of-pearl.

"Will you, Miss Lucretia?" he asked, looking toward the instrument.

"If you like, Mr. Clay," she replied demurely, seating herself at the spinet. Her facile fingers performed a tinkling minuet. Henry leaned over and placed a sheet of paper on the rack before her—a copy of Ben Jonson's "Drink to Me Only with Thine Eyes."

"Will you sing it?" he asked.

She played the opening chords and hesitated. His blue eyes implored, and she could not resist. She gave her auburn curls a slight toss as she looked up at him.

"Singing is not one of my accomplishments," she murmured.

As she started the melody, a hush fell upon the company. She had been right. Singing was not her forte, but her golden youth and buoyant lightheartedness made up for it. As she finished the first verse, her listeners joined in:

> "Drink to me only with thine eyes,
> And I will pledge with mine;
> Or leave a kiss but in the cup
> And I'll not ask for wine."

The evening passed swiftly. The hour grew late. Henry at last made his farewells and took his departure. James Brown saw him to the door and placed an affectionate hand on his shoulder.

"I trust you were not disappointed," he whispered.

Henry looked at him wordlessly. What was there to say? For the first time in their acquaintance he felt that the older man lacked finesse. Perhaps he was even a trifle crude, Henry thought.

When the door had closed behind their guest, the members of the Hart household prepared to retire. Colonel Hart watched them go up the winding stairway one by one. Lucretia was the last.

The servants had long since gone to their quarters. The master of the house snuffed out the candles in their holders as a last duty before following the others. He looked up at his daughter, who had stopped on the landing.

"James is right. Henry Clay will go far. He is a likely young man," the Colonel informed her.

A little smile played about the corners of Lucretia's patrician mouth. "He is a very stubborn one. I would say that he is determined to have his way and won't stop until he gets it."

He glanced at her curiously. "Perhaps you are right. I am not certain I know what you are talking about."

He snuffed out the last candle and, putting a fatherly arm about her slender waist, led her on upstairs. The deserted drawing room seemed singularly empty without the laughter and voices of the people who had filled it all evening.

Meanwhile their guest had not yet gone to his lodgings. Outside in the forest woodland that stretched to the north of the Hart home he was pacing back and forth alone in the night. Although his feet were soaked with dew, he was completely unaware of their condition. He was intoxicated with youth, ecstasy and love.

Hidden among the trees, he watched the last light on the upper floor of the house flicker and go out. He persuaded himself it was hers.

"Lucretia! Lucretia!" he murmured, rolling the enchanting syllables over his tongue.

He was not the same man who was daily becoming more familiar to the frequenters of the Lexington court. In the short time since he had been admitted to the Kentucky bar, the rising young lawyer, who spoke with a gravity and a wisdom beyond his years, was on the way to becoming an institution. His political admirers would scarcely have recognized the dreamy-eyed youth standing alone in the moonlight.

In accents most unlike those in which he was accustomed to address the court he whispered:

> "I sent thee late a rosy wreath,
> Not so much honoring thee,
> As giving it a hope that there
> It could not withered be."

5

HENRY BECOMES A HERO

"HENRY, YOU ARE A FORTUNATE INDIVIDUAL!" JAMES BROWN growled.

Henry regarded him with a questioning eye. "How do you figure that?"

The older lawyer held up a hand and obligingly counted off on his fingers. "For one thing, although a newcomer in Lexington, you set yourself against the most powerful lawyer in town in the dispute over a new state constitution. What happens? The voters go to the polls and call for a constitutional convention to be held next year—July, 1799."

Henry's brow darkened. "That does not mean they will approve Emancipation."

"If I know Kentuckians, they will not. But don't cross your bridges until you come to them. In the second place, before the heat of battle dies away, you find yourself side by side with Breckinridge, whom you opposed so bitterly on the constitutional question."

"If you mean the Alien and Sedition Laws, I do not see how any honest man can do anything but oppose them," Henry cried hotly.

"Many men are opposing them in the East, which is, to all intents and purposes, a different country from the West," Brown told him grimly. "There are few such persons in Kentucky, I am happy to say. It is good to see you standing shoulder to shoulder with John Breckinridge. He is a good man."

"Except on the question of Emancipation," Henry interposed.

Brown sighed. "Now, Henry, you must learn to live and
let live. There is an old Indian saying: 'You can never judge
another man until you have walked for one day in his
moccasins.' And you must confess that in his national politics
Mr. Breckinridge is idealistic enough to please even you."

"He was the founder of the Democratic Society in Lexington back in 1793, wasn't he?" Henry asked.

"He was a prime mover," Brown agreed. "Bless you, the
organization sprang into being so fast that no one knows
who began it. There were Democratic societies all over the
country, you know. They followed close on the heels of the
landing of Citizen Genêt."

Henry smiled. "I remember. I wore the tricolor cockade
myself, although I was only a fledgling clerk in the Chancery
Office at Richmond."

"Those were exciting times in Lexington," Brown told
him. "Nearly every man here wore the red, white, and blue
cockade. There were liberty poles on every street corner in
honor of our Revolutionary ally France, who had but recently broken the century-old bonds of monarchy. One
heard nothing but praise for France and damnation to the
Federalists who favored Britain. I suppose you might say
John Breckinridge led the Democratic forces in Lexington,
although many men were in hearty accord with him."

"He hasn't changed," Henry Clay said approvingly.
"Everyone knows that he despises the Alien and Sedition
Laws which President John Adams has managed to foist on
the nation."

"Those laws are ridiculous!" Brown exclaimed. "If they
are allowed to continue, the President of the United States
will hold unlimited power. After all, we fought the Revolution to do away with that sort of thing. Fourteen years for
an alien to become an American citizen! He'd be dead of old
age by that time."

"One would think old John Adams expected to find a Frenchman under every bed," Henry Clay observed.

"Even an intruder has a right to a fair trial," James Brown said with a smile. "The Alien Law provides no trial for a man if the President condemns him. It puts unchecked authority in the hands of one man. John Adams can set his seal of disapproval wherever he wishes and banish a man from these shores forever. It is unjust, tyrannical and un-American."

"Perhaps he fears a second Citizen Genêt," Clay interrupted. "I was newly arrived in Richmond when the fever over his arrival broke out. I well remember how eagerly we listened to reports of his progress after he landed in Charleston, South Carolina. For a time it looked as though, single-handed, he would lead us into war with England whether our country's government wanted it or not."

"Genêt certainly had his following," Brown agreed, "but he was an impetuous young man who acted in a manner unbecoming the minister from France to the United States. He aroused tremendous enthusiasm, but I am happy that he did not succeed in drawing us into war. We were too weak at that time to take such a stand. He was a trifle radical even for a French Jacobin."

"I'd rather find a French Jacobin than a monarchic Briton under my bed," Henry Clay declared, his blue-gray eyes twinkling. His voice grew serious. "The Sedition Law is no better. If Mr. Adams has the power to fine or imprison anyone who expresses an adverse opinion of the political party in power, then freedom of speech is at an end in America."

On July 4, 1798, Henry joined the crowd that was headed for the political rally at Maxwell's Grove on the southeast edge of the town. Feeling was running high. In the East, among the wealthy manufacturing class, John Adams had his following, but this was the heart of the Jeffersonian West where the majority of people thought poorly of him. Here a man in public life was judged by the quality of his political beliefs rather than the size of his purse.

The rank and file of men at Maxwell's Grove regarded Thomas Jefferson as a demigod and John Adams as a demon from the lower regions. What they wanted to hear on this gala day, when they were out for a holiday, was an orator who would voice their sentiments. They wanted a political speaker who would exalt their views on freedom, which the opposition scathingly referred to as Jacobinism, and they glowingly termed the Rights of Man.

Although the Federalists present were few in number, they were not timid. They did their best to present their speaker, who had barely opened his mouth before he was booed, catcalled and hurried off the scene.

Highly elated, the Democratic-Republicans asked George Nicholas to address the audience. He stood up before them, but it soon became evident that he could not hold the restless crowd. They wanted someone who was younger, more dynamic, more forceful.

"Clay!" a voice shouted. "Where is Henry Clay!"

"Clay! Clay!" they shouted.

The ambitious young lawyer heard them with a joyful heart. Here was his chance. Here was the opportunity for which he had been waiting. His maiden efforts in the courtrooms of Lexington had not passed unnoticed.

He willingly allowed himself to be hurried forward by eager hands. The bed of a two-wheeled farm cart was serving as an impromptu platform. Henry Clay mounted it and balanced himself with care.

He felt a thrill of exultation as he looked down into a sea of upturned faces. There were aristocratic landowners in fine broadcloth and linen ruffles. There were backwoodsmen in buckskin and linsey-woolsey. There were slaves in attendance upon their masters. All—even the slaves, in a sense— were Kentuckians and Americans. Henry Clay, realizing this, knew instinctively that they would listen to him.

For nearly an hour he spoke, keeping a constant watch to

judge the effect of his words upon his audience. He addressed the veterans of the Revolution. He called upon the spirit of '76. He appealed to those who preferred the abundance and plenty of America to the poverty and debt of Europe. He flung his defiance of the Federalist party with its autocratic principles into the teeth of its adherents in the audience, calling upon all patriotic Kentuckians to assert their belief in freedom.

When he finished and stepped down from the makeshift platform, the applause was thunderous. The sound was sweet to his young ears.

In the flush of enthusiasm, someone unhitched a pair of horses from an elegant carriage at the edge of the grove. Eager bystanders pushed Clay and Nicholas toward it and into it. Willing hands seized the shafts and triumphantly drew the two orators back into town and straight into the heart of Lexington.

The young lawyer could hardly realize that the demonstration was taking place. He turned unbelieving eyes to the veteran lawyer beside him. George Nicholas smiled.

"Their plaudits are very flattering," he agreed. "But remember—they can turn against you just as quickly."

"I'll take my chances," Henry Clay said. "I think I'm going to enjoy public life."

For him the high spot of the procession occurred when he spied the Harts' family carriage, which had pulled over to the curb to allow the triumphal procession to pass. Lucretia, in a blue moire gown that contrasted strikingly with her halo of auburn hair, sat back among the cushions and surveyed the noisy scene.

Her eyes caught Henry's as the carriages passed. With difficulty he restrained himself from leaping over the wheel and rushing to her side. Youth, love, fame! Bright banners led him on.

When the festivities had finally ended, he lost no time in hurrying to his room at Megowan's Tavern for a bath and a change of linen. In his haste, he left his room in a wild confusion most unlike his accustomed orderliness. He was eager to be off for the Hart house on North Mill Street.

When he reached there, Mrs. Hart was out making calls. The Colonel was at his ropewalk. The servants were conveniently absent at household tasks somewhere in the rear of the house. Lucretia alone was in the drawing room.

She ran to meet him, her hands outstretched. With difficulty he resisted an impulse to smother them with kisses. Instead he caught them in his own. He must not frighten this lovely creature, this exquisite bit of Dresden china, who, nevertheless—Heaven be thanked!—was all flesh and blood.

"I am so proud of you," she cried. "You were so tall and handsome as you bowed and waved from the carriage to the crowds on the streets. There were ten cheers for you to every one for Mr. Nicholas, poor fellow. To think how they adore you! Why, there is nothing they wouldn't give you, Henry. Nothing!"

Her words intoxicated him. All his defenses fell with a crash as he flung care and caution to the winds.

"There is only one thing I want, and the people cannot give me that," he declared fervently.

"And that is—"

"You for my wife, Lucretia!"

"I—"

"Wait," he pleaded. "I have loved you from the first moment I saw you. When I met you in this drawing room, I knew I must have you for my own or go through life half a man. I am only a penniless lawyer, but I have prospects. I can wait, my darling, but I cannot go on without knowing that you care. What were you about to say when I so rudely interrupted you?"

Lucretia looked tenderly up at him. Her face was wreathed in smiles.

"Only that I thought you'd never get around to asking me."

"Lucretia! I have known you only a little more than two months," he reminded her in a scandalized voice.

Thomas Hart's younger daughter gave a shameless laugh. "It didn't take me that long to realize I wanted to be your wife."

Henry Clay and Lucretia Hart were married the next year in the presence of their immediate families and a few friends. The ceremony took place in the drawing room of the Hart residence. The bride was eighteen. The groom lacked one day of being twenty-two. The date was April 11, 1799.

6

THE ROAD TO FRANKFORT

HENRY CLAY HAD SPENT A LONG, TIRING DAY IN THE OFFICE of John Breckinridge, the newly elected national senator who would leave on the morning coach for Washington, D.C. The jubilant Democratic-Republican forces had at last ousted the dying Federalist party and figuratively, at least, raised their banners in the nation's capital. Their idol Thomas Jefferson was in the saddle at last after a hotly contested battle with ambitious Aaron Burr, who had been forced to yield and satisfy himself with the vice-presidency on the thirty-sixth count of the electoral vote.

In Lexington—this year of 1801—John Breckinridge was leaving many of his law cases to young Henry Clay, who was more than happy to receive them. It had been over two years since Clay, a newcomer in the West, had opposed Breckinridge on the question of a new state constitution which would include a clause for the gradual emancipation of slaves. The two men, like the voters of Kentucky, had reached a compromise. A new constitution had been adopted, but Emancipation was a lost cause for the time being. Although in Henry Clay's heart it remained a goal, the young man sensibly adjusted himself to his environment and rapidly became a rising young attorney in the Bluegrass.

Since early morning John Breckinridge had been instructing him on various cases, suits, torts and other legal matters. At last he crossed his long legs and leaned his handsome head against his clasped hands.

"I guess that's it," he announced. "I've told you all I can, Henry. Now you're on your own! The roads are so poor between here and the East, I doubt whether I'll get back often, so you won't be able to depend on me. Besides, I shall be occupied with federal duties."

"I almost envy you," Henry said a little wistfully. "It will be a privilege to serve under Mr. Jefferson."

Breckinridge smiled. "I'll save a place for you. The country has need of young men like you, Henry."

"I'll have a difficult time trying to fill your shoes here," the younger man returned with youthful candor.

"Your own will fit you better," Breckinridge told him, a note of amusement in his voice. "Your fellow lawyers are still chuckling over that 'chew of tobacco' incident."

Henry grinned. "That was pure inspiration. I was sure the jury was on my side except for one man. From the look in his eyes, the prisoner being tried didn't have a chance. The rope was already tied around his neck. Then I remembered a little trick I had observed in a Richmond courtroom."

"So you asked the Judge's consent to indulge in a refreshing chew of tobacco," Breckinridge chuckled.

"And I was very careful—after I discovered I had left mine at home—to solicit it from the recalcitrant juror, who, after due deliberation, gave it to me."

The other man burst out laughing. "After which the said juror softened and listened for the first time to your persuasive argument."

"Of course," Henry Clay agreed. "If you want a man to like you, don't do something for him. Get him to do something for you."

"The ruse evidently worked," Breckinridge said. "In a short time, the jury returned a verdict of 'Not Guilty.' You are gaining a reputation as an outstanding criminal lawyer."

"One must know men as well as law. You know that, John. I have much to learn. To whom shall I go for advice when you are gone? My brother-in-law James Brown is bitten with the colonization bug and plans to move his family to Louisiana before long."

"There's a future down there," John Breckinridge said thoughtfully. "I wonder you haven't considered it."

Henry shook his head. "Lucretia is too attached to Lexington for me to give it a thought. And now our baby daughter Henrietta is one more link to tie her to her parents and friends. To tell the truth, I'm happy here myself. However, sometimes I get a bit weary of living so close to my in-laws, although I'm fond of them. I'd like to get a bit farther away and be able to call myself my own man."

Breckinridge laughed. "I have never heard anyone deny that Henry Clay is his own man. You must know you are an individualist, Henry."

Henry Clay hardly heard him. He was staring into the distance with a faraway look in his blue eyes. "There is a fine tract of land to the east of the town. I've had my eyes on it for some time. Much of it is in woodland—great, towering ash trees, for the most part. There's a gently sloping hillside that would be an ideal site for a home. I intend to have one there someday."

"The best of luck to you, my friend," John Breckinridge said, rising to his feet. "It may come sooner than you think."

"I hope you are right," Henry replied with a boyish smile. "I remember when I first arrived in Lexington I thought how comfortable I should be if I could make one hundred pounds, Virginia money, and with what delight I received my first fifteen-shilling fee. My hopes have been more than realized."

Breckinridge threw him a quizzical glance. "Report says that some of your affluence is due to your skill at poker."

Henry grinned from ear to ear. "One of my critics the other day said to my wife, 'Isn't it a pity that your husband gambles so much?' "

"What did Lucretia answer?"

Henry gave a hearty laugh. "She looked the lady up and

down coolly and replied, 'Oh, I don't know. He usually wins.' "

The year 1801 drew to a close. It found Henry a year older and an admittedly important member of Lexington's legal system. The "beardless boy," so-called in an exasperated moment by old George Nicholas, now deceased, was coming into his own. A continual procession of clients passed through his office doors. His fees piled up as court day succeeded court day, and farmers, frontiersmen and even the town's elite came to seek his services. His fame as a criminal lawyer was increasing.

Lucretia was not happy about the matter and was not slow in expressing herself.

"But not one of my clients has ever been sentenced to death," Henry remonstrated mildly. "You like a winner, don't you?"

"I have a winner," Lucretia informed him. "But you were made to do bigger things, my dear, than defend the participants of brawlings, shootings, stabbings—and outright murder."

"Every accused man has a right to a fair trial. There must be lawyers for the defense as well as for the prosecution," Henry grumbled.

Nevertheless, he gave more and more of his time to land-title suits. Old Judge Wythe had been right. In Kentucky even legal minds sometimes failed to straighten out land grants and claims. But Henry Clay seldom failed. Early and late he labored over tangled titles. In the process he inevitably accumulated large holdings, generally given him in lieu of fees. The young Virginia lawyer, who had come to Kentucky owning only the horse beneath him, was rapidly becoming a man of property.

Meanwhile his domestic life went on as usual in the modest brick house adjoining his father-in-law's. Little Henrietta closed her eyes in eternal sleep before she was a year old, but Theodore Wythe Clay arrived on the scene in 1802 and Thomas Hart Clay less than twelve months later.

In his climb up the ladder of success, Henry did not spare himself or his family. Indeed, at times he almost lost sight of his duties as a husband and a father. One day, coming home from a busy day at court, he found Lucretia in tears. "I know I shouldn't act like this, but I'm tired of never seeing you," she sobbed. "I'm tired of tending babies! I'm tired of keeping house! I'm tired of everything!"

He gathered her contritely in his arms. "I'm going to take you to Olympian Springs. Since your father owns the place, we certainly should enjoy it. Your mother and Aunt Chloe will take care of the babies. A few weeks under the trees by the river and some carefree days of cards, dancing and gossiping with our friends will be better medicine for you than all Dr. Dudley could prescribe."

True to his promise, Henry took his wife to the springs. It was a fashionable health resort, forty miles away on the Licking River, which old Colonel Hart had patterned after Bath and Brighton in faraway England. The color came slowly back to Lucretia's cheeks, and she was like her old self once more.

One day when the Lexington coach rolled up before the long, sprawling, one-story hotel, Colonel Hart climbed out. He resembled an elderly, rotund cherub as he panted his way up the broad steps of the veranda.

He planted a hasty kiss on Lucretia's forehead and shook hands with Henry. "I have news for you, my boy," he announced importantly. "Let us go to the summerhouse yonder so that I may speak with you in private. No, Lucretia—" he shook his head at his daughter, who had risen to accompany them. "This is not women's business. You will hear all about it in due time."

In the seclusion of the summerhouse Thomas Hart lost no time in stating the reason for his coming. His eyes were filled with a fatherly pride as he looked up at his tall son-in-law.

"I'll come straight to the point, Henry. Some of your friends in Lexington have nominated you as the representative from Fayette County for the state legislature. As you know, the election will be held at the courthouse next week. There is no time to lose. You must return at once and do your best to win."

Henry made no response. He was in a dream. He could hardly believe all this was true. Unsought, unasked, this stroke of good fortune had come to him. It almost seemed as though Fate must have had a hand—Fate, who had touched him on the shoulder when Judge Wythe had singled him out so long ago.

"You must return at once," Colonel Hart repeated.

Henry shook his head. An idea was beginning to form in his mind. He must have time to think, to plan. "You go by return coach, Father Hart. Say a good word for me wherever you can. I will be there before the election."

The Colonel frowned. "I don't understand. Your place is in Lexington."

Clay rose and laid a hand affectionately on the old man's shoulder. "I thank you from the bottom of my heart, sir, for bringing me this news. I want this office more than I can tell you, but I must act in my own way. I beg you to return—and have faith."

That night after Colonel Hart had ridden away, Henry walked up and down the pebbled path at the side of the hotel. Lucretia had long since retired. Outside her window the glow of her husband's cigar was visible until past midnight. Henry was planning his campaign. Knowing human nature as well as he knew law, he realized the value of showmanship and smiled to himself as he paced the winding walk.

It was the third and last day of the August election. Friends of Henry Clay were standing in despondent little groups outside the Fayette County Courthouse in Lexington. He had not yet put in his appearance. Then a rider on a lathered horse came galloping around the corner. The man pulled on the reins and brought the animal up on his haunches. Flinging himself out of the saddle, Henry dashed straight to the group of which Colonel Hart was the center.

"Am I too late?"

Colonel Hart gave his son-in-law a resounding thump between his shoulder blades. "Get up on that stump yonder and talk your way into office!" he roared. "I thought you were never coming."

The young man leaped up on the impromptu platform. In a few seconds he was haranguing a crowd that had increased after he appeared. His delay had been occasioned by a series of misfortunes, he told them. A broken axle—a lamed horse—

With a strong sense of the histrionic he concluded: "Had I known that I would be nominated for the legislature, I would have been in Lexington instead of at Olympian Springs. My deepest wish is to serve you, the people of my adopted state."

There was a hearty round of applause. Henry Clay was their favorite candidate. His audience had forgotten that not many minutes ago they had been saying that perhaps he did not appreciate the honor of being nominated. He had redeemed himself at this late hour by his dramatic appearance. Perhaps he had even heightened his chances.

The orator stepped down to the ground and mopped at his perspiring forehead with a fine linen handkerchief. He trusted he had saved the day.

As a shadow fell across his path, Henry looked up. A tall, rangy woodsman in hunting clothes and coonskin cap was standing with folded arms in Henry's way. He and the young lawyer measured each other from head to foot.

"So ye want t' go to th' legislature, young feller," the old pioneer drawled.

Henry laughed good-naturedly. "Yes, I do."

"Are ye a good shot?" the man demanded.

"The best in the country," Henry returned carelessly.

"Then, by thunder, we'll send ye," the man promised. "But first we must see ye shoot."

Henry gave a start. The truth was that he could not have hit a barn door at twenty paces.

"I—I never use any rifle but my own," he stammered.

The hunter shifted his quid of tobacco to his other cheek. "Take Old Bess," he urged, handing Henry his Kentucky rifle. "She'll do fer any marksman. One hunderd yards fer a squirrel and two hunderd fer a redskin. Ye can't fail with Old Bess."

Henry swallowed hard. He knew the value Kentuckians placed on marksmanship. Well, there was nothing to do but try. No other course was open.

"Put up your target!" he ordered.

The frontiersman nailed a target to a tree eighty yards away. It seemed three times that far to poor Henry. With an assurance he was far from feeling, he raised the rifle to his shoulder, sighted along the barrel and fired.

A cheer went up from the onlookers. The shot had hit almost dead center. If the young rifleman's hands were trembling slightly as he handed the smoking weapon back to its owner, no one was the wiser.

"Try it again, young fellow," a rival candidate's man urged. "That might have been just luck."

Henry gave him a haughty look. "When you can better my shot, I will."

There was a roar of laughter from the crowd. This was a bold man, and they liked bold men.

When the count at the polls was taken, young Henry Clay was the people's choice from Fayette County for the legislature.

In November, 1803, the young lawyer kissed Lucretia and the little boys good-by and rode off toward Frankfort, the small capital that nestled among the hills of the Kentucky River thirty miles away.

In the Statehouse he soon found himself in the general fever of excitement over Louisiana and the port of New

Orleans. The question was an old one, but it had recently sprung up with fresh fervor. The Mississippi River was the lifeline which the western country found vital for her trade. Between Kentucky and the eastern seaboard there were no decent roads on which Kentuckians could haul their corn, hemp and tobacco. New Orleans was not only a market, but also the seaport to the Atlantic coast. Once Spain had closed that city to the Americans. Now she had ceded it to France, and France was acting no better. Governor Garrard of Kentucky was ready to take steps.

The westerners decided that New Orleans must be an open port, and the conquest of that city was the main topic for discussion in Frankfort. For the first and last time in his life, Clay found himself actively involved in a military campaign. He was appointed an aide to General Hopkins, who was in charge of the projected expedition. Clay wrote his old friend Breckinridge that he was ready to "go with the crowd to endeavor to share the glory of the expedition."

Before preparations really got under way, the news arrived that President Jefferson had purchased Louisiana from Napoleon. In New Orleans, General Wilkinson ran up the American flag; and in Frankfort the legislators turned their attention to less dramatic but more practical matters.

Clay returned again to the legislature in the fall of 1804. This time he found a formidable opponent in the person of Felix Grundy, whom he had encountered during his first term in the legislature. Grundy, a man from the backwoods country south of the Kentucky River, had attempted to secure a repeal of the charter of the Kentucky Insurance Company. He had failed, but not before Henry Clay had come out in its defense.

The Kentucky Insurance Company, familiarly known as the Lexington Bank, was a growing concern in the state. Organized to write insurance, the company had been authorized in the fine print of its charter to do a banking business as well. The concern, headed by "Lord" William Morton of Lexington, had prospered from its start. It was only natural that it should succeed with such men as John Bradford for its cashier and Thomas Hart on its board of directors. Henry Clay was proud to represent it at Frankfort.

Before he set out for his second term, he was summoned by his father-in-law for a farewell conference. The old gentleman was getting on in years and even becoming a bit childish, but he still retained considerable business acumen.

"Now, Henry, you know what your friends are expecting of you when you return to Frankfort," he said a trifle testily.

Henry gave a quizzical smile. "To represent them fairly and honestly," he recited in a singsong naughty small boy's voice.

"Yes, yes," Thomas Hart agreed perfunctorily. He leaned forward and laid a hand on the young lawyer's knee. "You know, of course, that Felix Grundy worked overtime this past summer urging the destruction of the Kentucky Insurance Company. Now you must give him his comeuppance. If you don't, it's the end of our enterprise."

By now Henry was completely serious. "I shall do my best, Father Hart. No one should know better than I the value of our institution. Without it Lexington and the surrounding country would still be a part of the barter system instead of the growing little metropolis it is. It was inevitable that we should become dependent upon the bank. To put it mildly, it is no longer convenient for Mr. Bradford to be paid for subscriptions to the Kentucky *Gazette* in bacon or hams; for Mr. McCalla to trade his produce for a surplus of eggs; for the Reverend Moore to receive his salary in whisky; or for me to collect my fees in cattle—although I don't object to land."

"Exactly," Thomas Hart agreed, beaming. "That is what you must tell the opposition at Frankfort."

Henry looked thoughtful. "I doubt if they will listen to me."

"Then make them," Thomas Hart fumed. "Even those backwoodsmen south of the Kentucky River must yield to progress."

When Clay went to Frankfort in the fall of 1804, he was ready for the expected battle with Felix Grundy. The debates were furious; the contest bitter. The insurance company's charter issued in 1802 by the legislature was saved by one vote. Even that was small cause for rejoicing, however, for Grundy had managed to limit the company's banking powers.

A breathing spell for both parties followed. Then in November, 1805, Grundy made still another try. The repeal of the insurance company's charter seemed a certainty. Indeed, it passed both houses, was vetoed by the Governor, passed the House and was ready for the Senate where it seemed destined to succeed.

Felix Grundy and his cohorts were exuberant. In Lexington the faces of the insurance company's adherents were very long. The battle seemed lost.

Then questions began to arise. One met them on every street in Frankfort. No one seemed certain of their source, but they spread with the wind. What about the legality of land titles south of the Green River (Grundy's stronghold)? What about the fictitious names of the owners when it was common knowledge that the notorious "Green River Band" really held the said land grants? What about long overdue taxes on these fraudulently obtained lands?

These questions soon reached the Statehouse. Before the repeal of the insurance company's charter could take place, Henry Clay had introduced a bill to exact payment of the Green River debt. He spared no eloquence in its presentation. When the smoke of battle died away, the enemy's claws were clipped and the Kentucky Insurance Company's charter was saved.

Writing to John Breckinridge in the nation's capital, Henry stated modestly:

The attempt to Repeal the Lexington Bank is no doubt made known to you through our papers. The measure is finally in the Senate.

It was now 1805. At the end of the session Henry returned to his family, augmented now by another baby daughter—Susan Hart Clay. His law practice was waiting. Within the year Felix Grundy would leave the Kentucky scene and emigrate to Tennessee—Andrew Jackson's Tennessee. Meanwhile Clay, urbane, self-confident and ambitious, was acknowledged to be in the top tier of local politics. Instead of resting on his laurels, he looked eagerly about for more conquests. He knew now that politics was his field, his métier, his very life.

7

COUNCIL FOR THE DEFENSE

YOUNG PROFESSOR HENRY CLAY SAT WITH HIS EYES ON THE long wall clock, waiting for his class of embryonic lawyers to assemble. He had occupied the post of professor of law and politics at Transylvania College ever since James Brown had vacated it and moved to New Orleans. Clay's classes were always filled with fifty to seventy students, eager young men who saw in the popular attorney the prototype of their own success.

On this September morning in 1806 his glance swept the group assembling before him. Some were almost as old as he, while others had barely felt the razor's edge upon their cheek. He allowed himself a fleeting smile as he recalled that one of Lucretia's female relatives had referred to him in their premarital days as "Lucretia's pink-and-white young man."

When the class was assembled, an expectant hush fell over the room as Clay rose to his feet and surveyed the young men in silence for a moment. His classes were never stereotyped, dull or boring.

"Young gentlemen, I believe I promised you a review of the national political scene," he announced pleasantly. "I trust you are not too weary from your attendance last night at the theater, Vauxhall or Captain Fowler's Gardens."

A ripple of laughter ran over the room. All three spots were favorite gathering places for the young men of the town.

"It is necessary for individuals intending to embark upon the pursuit of the law to be thoroughly aware of the influences about them. I crave your indulgence if I speak of what you already know, but I shall act as though you are newly arrived upon this planet."

Almost from the outset of the Revolution there had been two political parties, Henry Clay told them. The Federalists, who were in power when General Washington became president, were entrenched in the East. They were the "monied few," the instrument of old "Alien and Sedition" Adams, the mouthpiece of pro-British John Jay. Indeed, the party itself was pro-British, in spite of the fact that America had thrown off the bonds of British tyranny barely twenty-five years ago.

In contrast, the Democratic-Republican party was the party of the people. Its domain was the young and vigorous West, although it had many adherents on the seacoast as the victory of 1800 for Thomas Jefferson had shown. Under the banners of the Democratic-Republican party this country, friendly to the French Republic, should rise to new and dazzling heights. There were no bounds to America's development.

"Who knows where we will go under Jefferson's leadership?" Henry Clay cried enthusiastically. "In time our empire should extend from sea to sea. Many people think that the West will one day include the domains of the haughty Spanish dons that border the Louisiana Purchase. Who can foretell the future? May we all share in the glories to come, gentlemen! Class dismissed."

The next day was Saturday. It found Henry Clay forty miles from Lexington at the rambling hotel owned by his father-in-law at Olympian Springs. He had ridden all night to get there. Now he was stretched full length on a couch in the family's private suite while Lucretia brought him an extra pillow, pulled the bell rope for a cooling drink and resorted to other wifely expedients that prevented him from dropping off to sleep.

Not that he wanted to sleep. Between half-closed eyelids as he watched her flutter about the room, he reflected that it was infinitely more pleasant here in this rustic atmosphere than in the hot, muggy town from which he had come.

Lucretia sat down on a low hassock and clasped her hands together. She seemed content with just looking at him. What a look of innocence there is about her, he reflected, in spite of six years of marriage and four babies.

"You will never guess what I heard in Lexington," he told her lazily.

"Napoleon has at last recognized his brother Jerome's marriage to Betsy Patterson," she ventured.

"No, no!" he answered impatiently. "That episode is over and done with despite the fact that you ladies attempt to keep it alive with your whispers and speculations."

Lucretia pouted prettily. "Well, she *is* the niece of Mrs. George Nicholas."

"And not important enough to be considered even a pawn by the Emperor," Henry reminded her. "From the beginning he disregarded her as though she never existed. I am afraid Madame Jerome and her infant son will have to reconcile themselves to life in her father's house at Philadelphia. But my news is about someone who has been in the public eye as much as the enchanting Betsy."

"Tell me," she begged.

"Aaron Burr," her husband answered. "He is in Lexington again."

"Did you see him?" she asked eagerly.

Henry shook his head. "He is staying at John Jordan's house on Upper Street. What his business is, no one knows, but the rumors are flying. Dan Bradford, the editor of the Kentucky *Gazette,* isn't at all happy over the situation. I talked with him a long time yesterday. Dan is inclined to exaggerate. He hasn't the rocklike stability of his father, old John Bradford, but he is a good editor, nevertheless. The paper is prospering under him."

"What did he say?" Lucretia asked again.

"Not much," Henry returned. "He just asked questions. Why has Mr. Burr bought land on the Washita River in Louisiana? Why does he continue to travel extensively in the West? Why does he have headquarters on Blennerhassett Island in the Ohio River?"

"Well, why?" Lucretia demanded.

Her husband looked thoughtful. "He *could* be planning colonization in Louisiana. He *could* be making ready to march into Mexican territory if the imminent war with Spain becomes a reality."

"Both of which are perfectly harmless schemes even if they are overly ambitious," Lucretia offered.

Henry nodded. "True enough. Neither scheme is what has set Lexington by the ears and started all the tongues of the town awagging. What would you say to a widespread rebellion—with the West seceding from the United States? With the aid of General Wilkinson, who was his comrade-in-arms long ago at the Battle of Quebec in the Revolution, Burr could control the Army, capture New Orleans, sweep into Mexico and become Emperor Aaron I."

Lucretia stared at him for a moment, her lips parted in astonishment. "Henry, that's perfectly ridiculous."

"That's just what I think," her husband agreed, swinging his long legs over the couch and rising to his feet. "Now I have news of real importance for you. Work on our new house is progressing at a rapid rate. We shall be moving in before long. What do you think of Ashland as a name for our house—for the ash grove that surrounds it, of course."

The Clay family returned to Lexington the next week. Henry made ready to go to Frankfort for the meeting of the fall legislature. Rumors about Aaron Burr were as thick as ever. Clay kept his eyes open and his ear to the ground. He was not long in discovering the power behind the

Western World, a scurrilous weekly newspaper that had been published in Frankfort since midsummer by two hack writers from the East.

"I might have known it," he told Lucretia. "The United States Attorney would attack an angel from Heaven if he thought said angel had Democratic-Republican leanings. I wonder if Jo Daviess added Hamilton to his name in honor of his dead hero, Alexander Hamilton. Daviess hates Burr not only for belonging to the Democratic-Republican party but also for killing Hamilton in what we anti-Federalists think was a well-justified duel. After all, how many insults and lies is a man supposed to take? Also, Daviess is Humphrey Marshall's brother-in-law. Those two have not stopped with impugning Burr. They have dipped back into the past and besmirched men of character like George Nicholas and Harry Inness by trying to revive the old Spanish plot that has been dead these many years. What depths men will stoop to!"

Clay referred to the so-called Spanish Conspiracy during the last quarter of the eighteenth century when, according to unsubstantiated rumor, prominent Kentuckians had been paid by Spain to influence the West in seceding from the remainder of the country. The gossip had long since been lulled to rest, but now and then an ugly echo would reach the ears of the populace.

With innocent eyes Lucretia looked at her husband. "Mr. Daviess and Mr. Marshall seem such nice gentlemen," she protested mildly. "Do you think they would really do anything to hurt Colonel Burr?"

Clay gave a short laugh. "My dear girl, when it comes to politics, you are a babe in the woods. You impute decency and honor to all men alike. All men do not have the same moral values."

Lucretia's face flushed. "I know very little about other men. I just know that you are above reproach."

"Thank you, my dear," Clay returned gravely. "You give me a great deal to live up to."

In spite of current gossip, Clay was surprised when Aaron Burr, former vice-president of the United States, sought him out a few weeks later at his Frankfort office. The man looked haggard and unhappy.

"Mr. Clay, I do not beat around the bush," he said. "I have met you at Chaumiere, the home of my dear friend Colonel David Meade. I hold you in great esteem as a member of the bar. I appeal to you as a fellow lawyer."

"I am at your service, sir," Clay replied courteously.

"A matter of only hours ago, as I alighted from my coach in Lexington in front of the Phoenix Hotel, I was waited upon by a writ-server from Joseph Hamilton Daviess, the United States Attorney. The said individual attempted to serve me with a warrant charging me, among other matters, with high misdemeanor."

"Good heavens!" Clay exclaimed. "Can Daviess be serious?"

"Quite serious," Burr answered gravely. "Fortunately for me, I realized that the document was spurious. I examined it carefully and discovered that Judge Inness of Frankfort has not yet given his opinion on Daviess' motion for my apprehension which was entered only yesterday in federal court."

"There is no time to lose," Clay told him. "These Federalists stop at nothing to embarrass and harass men of a more liberal political color."

"Exactly," Aaron Burr agreed. "While the falsely worded warrant certainly does not compel me to put in an appearance at Frankfort, I intend to go there. Do you think I am right?"

"Of course," Clay replied. "It is your only course."

"I thought you would say that," Burr answered. "Will you represent me?"

For an instant Clay stared across the table at the man who faced him. He remembered the afflictions through which the other had passed: the death of an adored wife with a lingering illness; the loss of the presidency to Thomas

Jefferson; the scurrilous political propaganda hurled at him by the Federalists, which had resulted in the fatal duel with Alexander Hamilton; the hue and cry of three states and the flight to escape the fate of hanging; the loss of prestige, power and position in the section of the country where he had lived for more than half a lifetime. And now came the accusation by the United States District Attorney, a man in whom the fires of political hatred burned brightly. Remembering all this, Henry felt a surge of sympathy for the man across the table.

"I shall be proud to represent you," he told Burr. "But you must be frank with me. What is your business in Kentucky, sir?"

The other gave an almost imperceptible start. "Mr. Clay, I am a hunted man," he said gently. "I can never return to the East and politics—and politics is my life. Perhaps I shall lead a company of young men to my Washita lands. If our chief executive should declare war with Spain, I would be ready to lead them with my sword. On the other hand, perhaps I shall hang out my shingle in some Tennessee wilderness and live and die a country lawyer. Let us say—my plans are uncertain."

On November 9 Henry Clay and his client made a surprise entrance into the federal courtroom at Frankfort. They were accompanied by prominent Kentuckians who had served with Burr in the Revolution. Another young lawyer, John Allen, completed the party. Henry Clay had seized the offensive. Public opinion seemed very much in his client's favor.

The first hearing was set for the following Tuesday. On that day when Henry Clay appeared to defend Aaron Burr, Joseph Hamilton Daviess in a surprise move rose and asked for the grand jury's dismissal.

"But why?" Clay demanded. "Mr. Burr has a right to a full and speedy investigation. His character is impugned. An innocent man is being persecuted."

A single witness, Davis Floyd, reputed quartermaster of Burr's armada of boats at Blennerhassett Island, was absent. The fact that he was attending the Indiana legislature made no difference. Daviess refused to go on with the trial.

After being entertained by the Governor and being visited by admiring Democratic-Republican legislators, Burr went on his way. Henry Clay's friends showed how they felt about the young lawyer himself when they elected him to fill John Adair's unexpired term in Congress. Henry was elated. The scene was broadening. Just over the horizon lay the national capital, and beyond that— He almost forgot the Burr affair.

But Jo Daviess did not forget. On November 25 he moved for another grand jury for the purpose of indicting Aaron Burr. If President Jefferson, to whom he had been writing frantic letters for nearly a year, chose to ignore him, then he alone would bring the traitor Burr to justice.

Senator-elect Clay received a plea from Burr to continue with his case. Inwardly Henry cursed the delay that kept him from proceeding to Washington, but ethically he knew his duty was to his client. He was more than a little flattered, too, by being sought out by a former vice-president. In the stillness of the night at Ashland, where he had moved into a partially finished house only a few weeks ago, Henry stared into the dying embers on the hearth and envisioned the years ahead. What might the defense of Aaron Burr mean to his future? He was confident the man was only the victim of Federalist rancor. And yet—

Clay struck his hand so forcibly on the table that Lucretia stirred in her sleep in the room beyond and small Thomas cried out in his trundle bed.

"I'll do it!" the master of Ashland exclaimed. "Just to be on the safe side, I'll do it."

The next day Henry Clay and Aaron Burr faced each other once more in Clay's office. The young Kentuckian leaned across the table that separated them. His blue eyes looked deep into Burr's enigmatic countenance. The younger lawyer's next remark was exceedingly forthright.

"Mr. Burr, I am about to embark upon another phase of a career to which I intend to devote a lifetime. Before I defend you again, may I have your assurance that you are innocent of any crime against your country?"

The man opposite Clay did not change his expression by even the flicker of an eyelid. He gazed at Clay for a while, then he spoke in his customary tones.

"Certainly, Mr. Clay. I will do better than that. I will give it to you in writing."

He reached for pen and paper and wrote rapidly for a few minutes. The young lawyer waited in silence. There was no sound but the scratching of the pen as the November sunshine streamed in through the long windows.

When Henry Clay set out for Frankfort, he carried with him a reassuring document. It read:

I have no design, nor have I taken any measure to promote a dissolution of the Union, or a separation of any one or more States from the residue. I have neither published a line on this subject nor has any one, through my agency or with my knowledge. I have no design to intermeddle with the Government or to disturb the tranquillity of the United States, or of its territories, or any part of them. I have neither issued nor signed, nor promised a commission to any person for any purpose. I do not own a musket nor a bayonet, nor any single article of military stores, nor does any person for me, by my authority or with my knowledge.

My views have been fully explained to, and approved by, several of the principal officers of Government and seen by it with complacency. They are such as every man of honor and every good citizen must approve.

Considering the high station you now fill in our national councils, I have thought these explanations proper, as well as to counteract the chimerical tales which malevolent persons have so industriously circulated, as to satisfy you that you have not espoused the cause of a man in any way unfriendly to the laws, the government, or the interests of his country.

With this paper in his possession, Henry brought the second trial of Aaron Burr to a swift conclusion. For four days the young man, assisted by John Allen, met Joseph Hamilton Daviess in a battle royal. Clay parried every thrust that Daviess gave and at times even made the Federalist lawyer seem a little ridiculous. As all the evidence was in and as Daviess' arguments grew more and more futile, the crowd became convinced that Burr was an innocent man.

Leaping to his feet, with his eyes blazing like those of a catamount, Henry Clay declared:

"Did I entertain the remotest idea of Colonel Burr's guilt, or of the truth of those charges which have been advanced against him, I should instantly denounce both him and his cause. But I believe the charges have not the smallest foundation of truth; I am confident they are only founded on idle rumors and the weakest credulity; that they are the machinations of malice, jealousy and suspicion."

At two o'clock of the fourth day the jury returned their verdict: "Not a true bill." The jurors had issued no indictment and furthermore they had absolved Burr of any designs against the peace and well-being of the country.

At last Henry Clay could resume his plans for the Washington journey. Refusing the fee tendered him by his client, who had been an honored member of the profession of the law, he accepted instead a few letters of introduction to prominent men in the nation's capital.

Without further ado he started on his way. One more successful case lay behind him. Greater times were ahead. He was about to enter the arena of national politics.

8

THE SCENE BROADENS

CHRISTMAS DAY HAD COME AND GONE BEFORE HENRY REACHED Washington, D.C. If the weary young man thought wistfully of Lucretia and the children as he ate an unappetizing meal in a squalid wayside tavern on Christmas Eve, he put them resolutely from his mind and set his thoughts upon the future.

He hoped that the opportunity to fill the vacancy in the Senate would be an open-sesame to an expanding career. If he had found the law a jealous mistress, as old George Wythe had warned him in the long-ago days, at least he had been faithful. Surely fidelity would pay in the end. But how long must he wait? Nebulous dreams and shadowy images flitted by him as he ate the greasy viands. The food was as poor as the beds were in the western country.

Clay had received a rude surprise at Chillicothe, Ohio. There was great excitement on the streets of the town over "Burr's Army," supposedly on its way down the Mississippi to seize New Orleans. Every citizen was loud in his denunciation of the traitor Burr. Clay listened aghast.

"One would never recognize him for the hero whom they feted and dined in Frankfort," he told himself.

He had hardly left Chillicothe when news came of Jefferson's Proclamation, which announced an unlawful expedition headed toward New Orleans and called for the arrest of the conspirators. Henry shook his head. Aaron Burr had seemed so completely innocent at the trial in Kentucky.

A few days after Christmas, Clay arrived in the capital at Washington, which was only a sprawling town on the Potomac. The city of magnificent distances planned by George Washington and Pierre Charles L'Enfant lay far in the future. Today the capital was still in its infancy.

The great White House on its rolling green slope was beautiful, even though it stood alone in its grandeur. Henry admired its generous proportions and long Palladian windows, remembering with a smile that frugal Abigail Adams had hung out her wash in the uncompleted East Room when she and her husband became the first occupants. No doubt much remained to be done to the interior but probably Mr. Jefferson with his simple Democratic tastes would not be so upset by the disorder of construction as the ultra-conservative New England Federalist and his wife had been.

Coming into Pennsylvania Avenue, which, in spite of its name, was only a rough country road full of ruts and holes, Henry looked at Capitol Hill ahead of him. The building that housed Congress was still unfinished. As he rode by, he studied it thoughtfully. Here he would spend most of his days from now until the end of Congress in the spring. How would he fare?

The young man found lodgings at Frost and Quinby's, one of the many boarding houses that dotted Washington. Although most of his fellow boarders were Federalist congressmen, they made him welcome in a manner that surprised him. Perhaps, he thought, they were too busy discussing Aaron Burr to examine or care about Henry's western politics.

The former vice-president's name was on every tongue. Rumors flew wildly. He was a rogue, a freebooter, a filibusterer. If his plans were successful, he would seize Congress, kill the President and become a second Napoleon.

"But I defended him only a few weeks ago when he was on trial in Kentucky!" Henry protested. "He swore to me that he is an innocent man. In spite of everything the prosecution could muster against him, a grand jury freed him."

One of the boarders eyed Clay speculatively. "Being a friend to Burr is a poor way to begin your Washington career. I think I'd clear myself with Mr. Jefferson if I were you."

"Apparently I've been duped!" Henry acknowledged. "When I saw Burr face to face, he appeared to be an innocent man—but now I'm not so sure."

The young senator from Kentucky hurried to the White House as fast as his legs would carry him. Although he had seen Mr. Jefferson more than once during his Richmond days, he felt his heart pound with excitement at the prospect of talking with him in person. He only wished that he were not here on such an unpleasant errand.

He paced nervously up and down the antechamber. He was about to face the Chief Executive of the United States of America who had publicly denounced Aaron Burr as a conspirator and a traitor. When he announced to the President his dealings with the unfortunate man, what effect would the information have upon his own budding career?

The door to Mr. Jefferson's inner office opened. "You may come in," an aide announced.

Henry squared his shoulders and walked through the door. The President was seated at a long table on which numerous papers and documents were spread out. Henry noted that Mr. Jefferson's once sandy-colored hair had turned to gray. His broad shoulders were slightly stooped with the years. He was dressed in his usual careless manner, but he had lost none of the bright charm of his youth.

He lifted his head and spoke courteously. "What can I do for you, my dear sir?"

The young Kentuckian took a step forward. "Mr. President, I am Henry Clay of Kentucky."

A smile of recognition broke over Jefferson's features. "The name is not unfamiliar to me. Our late friend Mr.

Breckinridge told me upon more than one occasion that he considered you a rising young man in the party. Then, too, you and I had a common mentor in Chancellor Wythe. A great man passed when he died this last year, Mr. Clay."

"I consider myself privileged to have known him," Henry said with sincerity. There was a brief silence before the young Kentuckian plunged into the business on which he had come. "Sir, I represented Colonel Burr when he was on trial in the capital of my state a few weeks ago."

Jefferson gave an involuntary start. "You? The pupil of George Wythe? Surely you were better grounded in patriotism than that."

Henry blushed to the roots of his flaxen hair. "Believe me, sir, it was lack of judgment—not lack of patriotism." From an inner pocket of his waistcoat he extracted a folded paper which he handed to the President. "He gave me this pledge of his innocence before his second appearance in court at Frankfort."

Thomas Jefferson put on his glasses and scanned the letter carefully. When he handed it back to the young man, his face was grim, but the lines about his mouth softened as he regarded his anxious visitor.

"You are very young, Mr. Clay, and Mr. Burr is a very clever individual. You are not the first man of integrity he has deceived. I have long considered him a crooked gun."

"But he seemed so guiltless!" Henry cried. "All of Kentucky was apparently on his side."

"Not quite all," Thomas Jefferson assured him dryly. "Your state's attorney general, Joseph Hamilton Daviess, has been bombarding me with letters for the past year."

"Oh, Jo Daviess!" Henry dismissed the name with a shrug.

The President's eyes held amusement. "I am aware that Mr. Daviess is a dyed-in-the-wool Federalist. But there are some honorable Federalists. On the other hand, not all Republicans are to be trusted. I have watched Aaron Burr for a long time. An overpowering ambition eats like a consuming growth at his breast. He has never forgiven me for the election of 1800. He had chosen the position of president for himself and maneuvered unsuccessfully to attain it. Since he could not win power honorably, he planned to swing the West out of the Union, seize New Orleans, capture Mexico and set up an empire. I fancy he would enjoy dictating terms to a thickheaded farmer, as I have heard he considers me."

"But, Mr. Jefferson, you are our president!"

The President nodded. "Thanks to General Wilkinson, Commander-in-Chief of the United States Army, I still am." He pointed to a drawer of the table behind which he sat. "I have here under lock and key full proof of the conspiracy. By now my men may have spread the net and arrested Aaron Burr."

Henry still looked dubious. "Down in Kentucky some folks don't think very highly of General Wilkinson."

Jefferson gave a wise little laugh. "Mr. Clay, I trust all men who serve their government, but I keep one eye open. General Wilkinson will always be stationed where I can watch him. Be grateful that your youth and unsullied reputation absolve you of all blame in the plot."

"I am deeply grateful," Henry assured him. "More grateful than words can ever say. Politics—dare I say statesmanship?—are the core of my life's ambition."

The President laid a hand upon his visitor's shoulder. Tall as Clay was, the older man looked down at him.

"Our new country has need of men like you. I am happy that you are serving her in your present capacity. I prophesy you will go far. Good day, Mr. Clay."

Henry Clay left the White House with a thankful heart for his narrow escape from the abyss of ruin and destruction. It had been a close call.

He immediately threw himself into the business on which he had come to the capital. Henry Clay, lawyer, had commitments which in no way concerned Henry Clay, senator. Various Kentucky clients had made up a purse of three thousand dollars for him. In return he was to look after their affairs in the Supreme Court of the United States. Accordingly he occupied himself when it was necessary in the dark, damp, musty basement room of the Capitol, where the nation's highest tribunal was located.

On the day after his conference with the President, he went to the Senate to be sworn in. The formalities having ended, he looked with interest at the semicircular chamber with its handsome carpets and cushioned chairs. He noted, too, the leisurely pace of proceedings as contrasted to the hustle and bustle of the Kentucky legislature. It was the difference between the old cultivated East and the new raw West.

Almost immediately he formed a friendship with Senator William Plumer, a moderate Federalist from New Hampshire and a fellow boarder at Frost and Quinby's. Attracted by the westerner's personality and winning ways, and despite their political differences, the older man appointed himself Henry's guide through the Congressional maze.

Through Senator Plumer young Mr. Clay met most of the other senators. Among them were Timothy Pickering and Uriah Tracy of New England, who looked askance at their colleague's friendship with the young Democratic-Republican from the West; James Bayard of Delaware, said to be the best orator in the Senate; and John Quincy Adams, Puritan son of a Puritan father.

Henry found that the Senate was made up of middle-aged and elderly men. They provided a balance wheel for the younger, more impetuous members of the House of Representatives. Clay was the youngest senator. The fact that last November he had lacked seven months of being thirty years of age, the constitutional age for national senators, had not deterred the Kentucky legislators from appointing him. They had needed a man to fill the unexpired term of peppery John Adair, who had resigned his post in a moment of anger. Henry Clay's shoulders, in spite of their youth, were broad enough to bear the mantle. *Ergo,* they appointed him.

Clay thought of this as he looked up and down the Senate chamber on the morning of his first appearance there. He knew he must make up in dignity and decorum what he lacked in years.

There must be rules in order to govern, he reflected, but rules may be broken at the right time by the right men. A strong man will always cut the Gordian knot.

At times Clay looked with longing toward the spirited atmosphere in the House of Representatives. There the men were his own age. The very tone of the place was charged with vigor and strength. The young men seemed alive in every fiber of their being. They displayed it in energetic debate and lusty speeches.

Here in the Senate the elderly members moved with caution, deliberation and precision. Prudence was the order of the day. Henry longed to spring to his feet and electrify them with his oratory, but he refrained. He had come to fill a senator's shoes, and he would fill them to the best of his ability. However, he was young, ambitious, gregarious and there was life to be lived.

Henry spent few evenings at his dull boarding house. There were dinners and balls. There were receptions and levees. And, of course, there was the game of poker, a diversion in which Mr. Clay excelled.

Of interesting people there was no end. Joel Barlow, the poet, who was also an astute man of business; Robert Fulton, the inventor, forever talking about his steamboat; Benjamin Latrobe, the architect of the new wing of the Capitol; and Turreau, the swashbuckling ambassador from France.

And to be sure, there was captivating Dolley Madison, wife of Secretary of State James Madison. Little Jemmy, as they called him, was a small, dried-up figure of a man who could be "incomparably pleasant" in private company. Clay spent a great deal of time at the Madisons'.

Dolley was a fine figure of a woman. All Washington agreed to that. Henry, always a favorite with the ladies, was soon laughingly claiming her as "kissin' kin" from Virginia. Both had many common acquaintances in Hanover County, where they had spent their childhood.

If Henry Clay played in the evenings, he worked during the day. He had been sent to Washington for a purpose, and he intended to give a good account of himself.

His maiden speech related to the building of a bridge across the Potomac. The young man, who was put on four different committees during this term of Congress, soon attracted wide attention. Federalist John Quincy Adams of Massachusetts noted that Clay was "quite a young man—an orator—and a Republican of the first fire."

Clay's heart was centered on internal improvements. Having spoken for the Potomac Bridge bill, he advocated government aid for a canal between the Chesapeake and Delaware bays. As a man from the western country with its poor roads and bad communications, he knew the need for internal improvements. Already his mind held the conviction that the federal government was stronger and must aid the states. To his great disappointment, the measures were shelved and not acted upon.

In spite of all his Washington interests, his heart turned toward the Bluegrass. To his father-in-law he wrote: "After all that I have seen, Kentucky is still my favorite country. There, amidst my dear family, I shall find happiness in a degree to be met with nowhere else."

"The business of Congress is about completed," Henry said to his friend Senator Plumer as they walked toward their boarding house one cold night in February.

The older man shook his head. "It has hardly begun, my dear fellow. If you noticed, we carefully avoided questions of foreign policy. They must be settled sooner or later. Americans will not endure forever the impressment of their seamen to swell Britain's navy in her war with France. That has

been going on ever since the outbreak of hostilities between
Britain and France in 1803. I tell you there is serious trouble
ahead. I fear we cannot hope to remain at peace. We may
yet be drawn into the maelstrom of a foreign war. Congress
has a heavy burden next year."

Henry's face darkened. He turned up the collar of his
greatcoat to break the force of the wind at his back.

"I have no love for England," he said decisively. "The
most frightening memory of my childhood is the day when
Colonel Tarleton and his redcoats swept down on our poor
little Virginia farm, seized our livestock, wrought wanton
destruction on our farmhouse and threatened to desecrate
my father's grave—he had been buried only three days before
—until my mother stood her ground and shamed them into
leaving. I was only four at the time, but I have never forgotten."

"A good many captive Americans in the British Navy will
never forget, either," Plumer rejoined. "England can't seem
to understand the American mind. They should. It comes
from the same stubborn Anglo-Saxon stock as their own,
which values freedom above life itself."

The lights of the boardinghouse twinkled ahead of them.
A warm supper and congenial companions were waiting.
Henry felt his animosity slipping away at the thoughts of the
creature comforts ahead.

"What you say may be true," he agreed. "However, I shall
not be here. I am only filling an unexpired term. Besides, I
have business of my own. Benjamin Latrobe has promised
to draw up a set of plans for the brick house I intend to build
as my permanent residence at Ashland, my Bluegrass farm.
Furthermore, I have made plans along with some other Kentuckians to import the stallion Buzzard from Europe. Colonel Tayloe tells me he is the finest horse on the Continent.
There are a thousand and one things to be done on my farm.
I have not seen my wife and children for more than two
months, and there's a fifth Clay expected in April. I'm afraid
the capital will have to do without me next year."

9

PROVING GROUND

As soon as Henry Clay returned to Kentucky, he discovered that local politicians were fanning the flames of the Aaron Burr trial, which was due to open on May 22 in the House of Burgesses in Richmond, Virginia. When that was under way, the Democratic-Republicans of Lexington, along with those of the rest of the country, became gradually convinced that their one-time hero was guilty of the crime of treason. Meanwhile the trial at Richmond continued to drag on. It was really a fight to the finish between Thomas Jefferson, head of the executive branch of the government, and John Marshall, head of the judicial branch. Two giants of opposite political parties were trying their strength.

The Federalists in Kentucky lost no time in turning the situation to their advantage. Humphrey Marshall, a leading member of the party and a brother-in-law of John Marshall, adroitly led his associates to point the finger of scorn at the Burrites, as he labeled Henry Clay and all other Democratic-Republicans who had once sympathized with the former vice-president. A popular toast that went the rounds in federal circles was: "The Tree of Liberty! May it never produce another Burr."

By now Clay felt beyond the shadow of a doubt that the man he had once defended was guilty to the core. Although the young lawyer regretted his earlier action at Frankfort, he had cleared himself with Mr. Jefferson. When the Federalist politicians of the state tried to smear him because he

had once befriended Burr, he went his way with little regard
for the epithets hurled at him. The people proved their
feeling for him when they re-elected him to the state legislature even before the former vice-president was acquitted on
a technicality in September. The general public, who believed him guilty, took a dim view of his freeing.

There was much work for Henry Clay before he could
give a thought to Congress again. Outwardly calm, he was
a badly shaken young man, grossly deceived, he now admitted, by the man he had once believed to be innocent.

One day in early fall, before he left for the state capital,
he was enjoying a leisurely breakfast at Ashland. The
rasher of bacon on his plate had come from his own smoke-
house. The feathery omelet was made with eggs from his
own hens. Even the flour in the hot biscuits had come from
wheat grown on Ashland's broad acres. Politician though he
was, there was enough of the farmer in him to appreciate his
home-grown products.

But Lucretia was plainly disturbed. She scarcely touched
the food on her plate. "How can you just sit there?" she
cried, her cheeks flaming. "That dreadful Mr. Marshall is
saying terrible things about you. And the Lexington *Re-
porter* is just as bad."

"Naturally," Henry replied coolly. "After all, it *is* a
Federalist newspaper." He looked through the pile of opened
letters beside his plate and selected one. "Listen to what our
dear James says from New Orleans. He writes, of course, to
congratulate me on winning the race for the legislature.
Nancy sends love to you. Ah, here it is. 'I pray you to quit
public life, or muster up sufficient philosophy to bear up
under all the hard names with which you will be christened
. . . as long as you retain your brains and your independence you will be abused.' "

Lucretia appeared somewhat mollified. "I suppose what
he says is true."

"Too true," her husband agreed. "You married a politician, my dear. I'm afraid you will have to become accustomed

to these attacks. I consider them of small importance. *They do not worry me.*"

"Then what does worry you?" Lucretia inquired with concern in her voice.

"The war between France and England," he declared between set teeth. "Matters are far worse than they were last spring. They are fast becoming intolerable. No American ships are safe. Whenever he takes a fancy, Napoleon seizes our ships in French ports in order to secure revenue for his armies. We receive even worse treatment from England. Her officers arrogantly board our neutral vessels on the high seas and kidnap American sailors. I grant you that now and then they seize deserters from the British Navy, but for the most part they impress honest, loyal Americans. 'Once an Englishman, always an Englishman,' they claim. Great heavens! Did we fight for our freedom and win the Revolution in vain?" Clay pushed his plate aside. His concern had taken away his appetite.

"The *Chesapeake-Leopard* affair was the last straw," he declared. "America must take a stand, or we shall be the laughingstock of all civilized nations."

He referred to an incident which had taken place off the coast of Virginia in early summer when the British ship *Leopard* had opened fire on the American frigate *Chesapeake*. Twenty-one Americans were killed or injured. The commander of the *Chesapeake* had been forced to give up four of his crew to the British. This was merely one more incident of the shameful practice of impressment. It only served to intensify the mounting indignation of the country.

In the middle of his angry remarks, Henry's eyes fell upon the anxious face of his gentle young wife, who sat across the table from him. Instantly he felt contrition. Wars might rage and America might be endangered, but Ashland was Lucretia Clay's kingdom and her husband was the center of it.

"Oh, pshaw!" he said reproachfully. "Why am I running on like this? It's a beautiful day, and there are a thousand things to see to on the farm. I must get everything in order before I leave for Frankfort. After that, you must manage Ashland alone for a while."

Lucretia's face brightened. "You know that's no hardship, Henry. I love everything about the farm."

Rising to his feet, he kissed her lightly as he passed. "You're a better farmer than I am. At least, that's what I hear the servants think."

"How can you say such a thing?" she protested, blushing with pleasure.

"Because it's true," Henry assured her. "My interests lie chiefly with the horses and livestock—that is, when they aren't concerned with law and justice. But this morning I think I'll leave the running of the nation to Mr. Jefferson. After all, it's his job."

He paused before leaving the room and looked back. His tall form almost filled the doorway. His face was very earnest.

"There's talk of an embargo, you know. Maybe that's the answer. Mr. Jefferson seems to think so. Let the sugar, molasses, coffee, tobacco, cotton, salt fish, wheat, corn, furs, rum and lumber stay on this side the Atlantic. Maybe the French and the English wouldn't like that so well."

A short time later Lucretia looked out of a back window to see her husband pacing back and forth under the majestic trees in the rear woodland. She sighed with relief. He always seemed to find calmness and strength in those strolls. His feet were beginning to wear a path known in the servants' quarters as "Mr. Clay's Walk."

The war spirit had not abated when the Kentucky legislature opened. Through blind and misguided patriotism a motion was introduced to forbid the use of all citations of British law in the Kentucky courts. This would amount to abandoning the common law, which was the bedrock of the entire legal system. In spite of the fact that he had no love for England, Henry Clay opposed the measure with his usual mixture of common sense and stubbornness. He finally persuaded the legislature to adopt a compromise which prohibited only those British decisions made after July 4, 1776.

"I do not care to throw out the baby with the bath," he said whimsically to Lucretia, who was giving small Anne her morning tubbing.

Lucretia broke into laughter as she pushed back the damp hair curling in small tendrils about her face. "Henry, how can you!"

Her husband's face was grave. "I must laugh sometimes or go mad. Things are bad at Frankfort, 'Cretia, and they are worse in the nation. The embargo is failing. By its terms no American ships can leave American ports to deal in foreign trade. The ships are rotting in their docks. Trade is at a standstill. Men are out of work. All New England is condemning Mr. Jefferson, and Europe seems to be getting along without us. Now if the shoe were on the other foot, it might be a different story. If we could refuse to buy imports from them, perhaps the thinness of their pocketbooks might bring them to their senses."

He slapped a hand sharply down on the table and sprang to his feet.

"That's it!" he exclaimed. "Why haven't I thought of it before? We will wear homespun rather than trade with the scoundrels. If the plan works in Kentucky, it will spread throughout the nation."

In due time Henry introduced the "homespun resolution" on the floor of the House of Representatives. It provided for the use of only clothes of domestic manufacture for the members of the legislature. Clay hoped by this means to bring England and France to their senses.

Humphrey Marshall, of course, opposed the plan. The fact that Henry Clay was for it was enough for him. If "Prince Hal," as Clay's followers were beginning to call him, asserted that white was white, the "Prince of Devil's

Hill" (the opposition's name for Marshall) would conclude at once that it was black.

When Clay, dressed in a suit of homespun woven from wool grown on the backs of his own Merino sheep at Ashland, appeared on the floor of the House, Marshall (who heretofore had worn homespun) lost no time in appearing in a suit of the finest imported broadcloth.

The struggle had begun. The debates which followed on the floor of the House reached a new high in epithet and abuse in an era when men in public life were especially adept in the use of words as weapons.

Marshall called Clay a liar. In an instant the two were engaged in a violent struggle. In the eyes of more than one representative they resembled two mountain bucks struggling for the supremacy of the herd. Several members rushed forward and stopped them.

In his bedroom at the Eagle Tavern that evening Henry handed his friend John Campbell a folded paper.

"My challenge," he said briefly. "You will oblige me by delivering it to Mr. Marshall."

Major Campbell hesitated. Dueling was forbidden by law in the state of Kentucky. Furthermore, as a member of the legislature Clay would receive especial censure if he engaged in the illegal practice.

Henry seemed to read his thoughts, and though he spoke calmly, there was an underlying tenseness in his voice.

"I am suggesting to Mr. Marshall that we cross the Ohio River at Shippingport and thus remove ourselves from the jurisdiction of the state. I do not approve of dueling, my friend, but there comes a time when a man must defend his honor. This time Humphrey Marshall has gone too far. No man calls Henry Clay a liar without taking the consequences. I may be a public servant, John, but I am a human being first."

Again he appeared to read the query in the eyes of Major Campbell. "My family is well provided for in case of any unfortunate eventuality." He turned aside with a faint smile. "You may be interested to learn that I have already dispatched a messenger to my brother-in-law Tom Hart with a request to procure for me the best brace of pistols he can find in Lexington."

On January 19, 1808, the duel between Clay and Marshall occurred at the appointed time and place. Neither of the principals was seriously wounded, but honor seemed satisfied and the two enemies declared a truce.

From the home of a friend in Louisville, Clay wrote:

Dr. Clark:
I have this moment returned from the field of battle. We had three shots. On the first I grazed him just above the navel—he missed me. On the second my damned pistol snapped, and he missed me. On the third I received a flesh wound in the thigh, and owing to my receiving his first fire, &c., I missed him.

My wound is in no way serious, as the bone is unhurt, but prudence will require me to remain here some days.

Yours,
HENRY CLAY

Until he resumed his seat on February 8, the irrepressible Henry enjoyed a vivacious convalescence, playing poker with his well-wishers to while away the time.

The early part of 1810 found him back in Washington. Again the Kentucky legislature had appointed him to fill an unexpired term in the Senate. This time there had been many more matters to settle in Lexington before he could leave for the capital. By now he had become a very solid citizen, as well as a father for the sixth time. The new arrival was named Lucretia for her mother.

Although Clay was not a church member, he had assisted the Reverend Moore in organizing Christ Episcopal Church, to which Lucretia belonged. He was a trustee at Transylvania College, where he had taught law for two years.

He owned a tavern in Lexington and a part-time interest in a hemp company. His farm occupied much of his time, although Lucretia could and did run it successfully in his absence.

Then, too, the local scene was changing. John Breckinridge had died in 1806, even before Henry's first visit to Washington. Old Colonel Hart had passed from the scene in 1808, and his son and namesake, Thomas Hart, Jr., had followed him in late 1809. Members of the Hart family looked to Clay more and more for counsel and advice. In short, Henry Clay was a man of parts.

He took care of his personal affairs and reached Washington in time to address the Senate on Washington's Birthday, 1810. There was no doubt about where he stood. He was Young America on the march. He was the spirit of the New West—the epitome of self-confidence, strength and patriotism.

He admitted he was weary of attempting to deal with Britain. The impressment of seamen had not abated, but rather than settle for a false peace he declared, "I am for resistance by the sword!" And he continued, "The conquest of Canada is in your power. I trust I shall not be deemed presumptuous when I state, what I verily believe, that the militia of Kentucky are alone competent to place Montreal and Upper Canada at your feet."

During the next recess a handsome, black-haired young man came forward to shake his hand. He was John C. Calhoun from South Carolina.

"I agree with every word you say," he told Clay enthusiastically. "There must be no compromise with England."

Congress felt differently, however. So did John Randolph of Virginia, the tall, thin, eccentric member of Congress who boasted that he was descended from Pocahontas. Although he sneeringly referred to the young man as "the Cock of Kentucky," the white flame of Clay's spirit was spreading when the session closed for the summer.

Before Congress reconvened the next winter, President

Madison had annexed West Florida. Since the days of the Louisiana Purchase in 1803, no one seemed to be quite certain who owned West Florida. Spain claimed it. So did America. Since it was off Napoleon's hands, he was not greatly concerned. The disputed territory became an attraction for land-hungry settlers, adventurers and frequently renegades.

Tiring of Spanish rule, the colonists rebelled in September, 1810, captured Baton Rouge and declared themselves independent. Then they asked to be annexed to the United States. President Madison, since Congress was not in session, acted boldly. He proclaimed that West Florida belonged to America by right of the Louisiana Purchase. (He seemed to forget that the claim had been disputed ever since 1803.)

When Congress met in December, the Federalists condemned the act. The Democratic-Republicans condoned it. In fact, they approved it.

Henry Clay defended the Administration. Did we want Great Britain, Spain's ally, to acquire the territory, he asked. We must take it now, even if war with England resulted.

The young Republicans were with him. To a man they cast covetous eyes on West Florida.

Meanwhile the war fever mounted. The people of the United States seemed to be waiting only for a spark to set off the conflagration. That spark came, after the Eleventh Congress had adjourned, in May, 1811. The American frigate *President* was fired upon by the British sloop-of-war *Little Belt*. The American ship returned the attack with a loss to the enemy of thirty-two killed or wounded. The tables were turned and the *Chesapeake* was avenged.

10

THE YOUNG WAR HAWKS

WHEN HENRY CLAY WENT TO WASHINGTON IN NOVEMBER, 1811, the city had taken on a new air. Tremendous enterprises were under way. The war spirit which had been prevalent during the preceding months now dominated the scene. The men who represented the trade and manufacturing interests of the East tried in vain to avert the coming storm in the belief that war with England would be disastrous to a new and struggling nation. For the most part these men were old, conservative and inclined to preserve the *status quo*, but their course was uncertain. Just before his term expired in the spring of 1809, President Jefferson had signed an act repealing the embargo. His successor, President Madison, during his first year in office, had hoped for a solution of the country's difficulties with the Non-intercourse Act, which permitted American ships to deal with any countries in the world except England and France and her allies. The move did no good. France continued to seize American cargoes in French ports, and England still impressed American sailors. If rumor were true, the English were inciting the Indians to the warpath on the northern borders of the United States. President Madison was beset with difficulties on every side and hardly seemed to know what to do.

But if leadership was weak and vacillating in some quarters, it was strong in others. The West and the South had sent a group of young men to Congress who knew what they wanted and intended to get it. They had been elected from their various states on a rousing war platform.

The Young War Hawks, as they were called, had an average age of thirty-one. They were strong, vigorous, militant and dynamic. The leaders among them were Felix Grundy of Tennessee, John Adams Harper of New Hampshire, William Lowndes, Langdon Cheeves and John C. Calhoun of South Carolina, and Richard Mentor Johnson and Henry Clay of Kentucky. At Mrs. Wilson's boarding house, where they lodged, they lost no time in choosing a head. The lot fell to the young man who had made an oration on Washington's Birthday before the Senate last year—"the Western Star"—Henry Clay.

The subject of their choice accepted the honor from their hands with all the fervor of youth. Twice he had filled out the unexpired terms of other men in the Senate. Now he was elected to the House of Representatives, where a young man should be. It was not the first time that Fortune had smiled in his favor.

His wife and children—Theodore, Thomas, Susan, Ann, Lucretia and Henry Clay, Jr. ("the stoutest son we ever had," his father had written a friend at his birth) aged seven months—had accompanied him to Washington, but he saw them all too seldom. Most of his waking hours were spent with the other Young War Hawks. They had a prodigious task before them.

Congress had barely convened when news came of the Battle of Tippecanoe in the Indiana Territory. The Indian chief Tecumseh had organized many of the tribes of the Northwest in a confederacy by means of which he hoped to drive all white men south of the Ohio River and east across the Appalachians. When William Henry Harrison, governor of the territory, became aware of this plan, he lost no time in raising an army of volunteers and setting out for Tippecanoe, Tecumseh's headquarters on the Wabash.

The Indians surprised the white men in an unexpected attack, and pandemonium resulted. Although the Indians were driven back, they had killed thirty-eight and wounded one hundred and fifty whites. It was a doubtful victory, but the press and the War Hawks made the most of it.

"This is a British war!" they cried. "The British fur traders are behind these Indian uprisings! We shall all be murdered in our beds! We must go to war to avenge the heroes of the Wabash!"

In the meantime the War Hawks had swept the House before them and enthusiastically elected Henry Clay Speaker on the day that Congress opened. Victory for Young America was in the air.

Speaker Clay took his seat in the chair with an elation he had difficulty in hiding beneath a dignified exterior. He had been nearly thirty-four years journeying to this point and he felt exuberant.

He fancied he could hear Chancellor Wythe's dry, crisp tones saying, "Not politics, but statesmanship. Statesmanship!"

Were they ever entirely separable, he pondered. Down in Kentucky it was hard to tell where one began and the other left off. Only Lucretia high up in the balcony caught the triumphant light in his clear blue eyes.

But those eyes grew cold and icy as they surveyed the lackadaisical atmosphere of the oval-shaped room with its high sandstone columns. The air of informality that pervaded the House ill became the legislative halls of a nation. There was nothing resembling expectancy or respect. Small groups gathered here and there in laughing conversation. Up in the balcony modishly dressed ladies waved to masculine acquaintances on the floor.

Clay rose to his feet, tall, slender and commanding, and pounded with the gavel. "The House will come to order!"

There was no mistaking the authority in that tone. In a matter of minutes he had sent a courteously worded message to a sleeping member to keep awake or go home to bed. As quickly he had ordered the hunting dogs led out which John Randolph was pleased to bring with him. This time the eccentric gentleman from Virginia did not demur as he had done on other occasions.

There was no doubt about it. The new Speaker was fearless. This session of the House would be decidedly different from others that had preceded it. It was not a social occasion but a strictly businesslike affair!

On November 5 President Madison delivered his message to a joint session of Congress. It informed the people of little they did not already know. He merely reviewed the country's poor relations with Great Britain and emphasized the need for national security.

That was enough for the War Hawks. Clay at once put all of them on all important committees. The time had come for action. The War Hawks knew that the United States must increase the Army and Navy. They knew that the country must go willingly into war, but first the people must be made aware that war was necessary. Clay's group had a strong ally in Secretary of State James Monroe.

"Gentlemen, *we must fight*. We are forever disgraced if we do not," he had said on one occasion.

However, the opposition was not to be underestimated. The New England Federalists apparently sympathized with Englishmen more than they sympathized with their own countrymen in the West and the South who felt themselves in danger from the red man's tomahawk and flaming arrow. The majority of the Democratic-Republicans would follow the President. But where was the President going?

The War Hawks turned all their powers of persuasion on Madison, but they need not have concerned themselves. Public opinion countrywide was fast moving in their favor. The Battle of Tippecanoe had stirred Americans to demand action. Late in December the Senate introduced a bill to raise an additional military force; when it reached the House, Clay stepped down from the chair, as he was to do so often during the course of a lifetime, and spoke strongly in its favor. In the ensuing weeks he would support a bill for volunteers; one to allow the state militia to invade Canada, another to increase the strength of an almost nonexistent navy and still another to increase taxes. The war party was in the saddle at last and ready to ride.

One cold winter night Clay came face to face with his old enemy Felix Grundy as he was leaving the Capitol.

The Kentuckian gave a wide, friendly grin. "It's odd being on the same side of the fence with you, Felix, but I must say it's easier."

The phlegmatic Tennesseean grunted. "If you fight the opposition as hard as you fought me back in Frankfort in 1805, we should soon see results."

"Since we've combined forces, we should wield some influence," Clay said with a chuckle.

The two men went on their way, talking earnestly. The streets were deserted except for a few pedestrians hurrying home to supper.

"Let's see where we are," Clay said, counting on his long, thin fingers. "One. We have increased our army from four thousand to twenty-five thousand. Two. Congress has authorized fifty thousand militia, which may be used to invade Canada. Three. We have at least the beginning of a navy. Four. We have voted more taxes—not enough to carry on a war, but at least more."

Grundy shook his head. "But the President. There can be no war until he asks for it, and apparently he is unwilling to make the move."

Henry stopped and fixed his piercing eyes on Grundy. "I do not give up easily, my friend. In fact, I do not give up."

His companion gave a short laugh. "No one should know that better than I."

On June 18, 1812, President Madison, forced by public opinion, at last declared war on England. The War Hawks were jubilant though they fully recognized the gravity of the situation. The cause in which they believed was advancing.

Mr. Clay went home to Kentucky that summer, but he spent little time in the Georgian mansion known as Ashland.

It was a welcome haven for Lucretia and the children after the hurry and bustle of Washington, but the master was far too occupied to take his ease.

He found Lexington, indeed all of Kentucky, in the throes of war preparation. There were public dinners. There were celebrations. There was volunteering. There was drilling to the sound of fife and drum. His old friend and colleague John Allen raised a regiment—"as fine men as ever drew a trigger." Lucretia's brother Nat commanded a company of one hundred infantrymen. Kentuckians were panting to meet the enemy.

Americans prepared to march on Canada. At first, all went well. Aroused to fever pitch by reports of Indian depredations, the volunteer armies set off for the Canadian border. The red men would be subdued, Canada seized, and a proud enemy brought to her knees. Henry Clay—Harry of the West —had prophesied an easy victory. The Kentucky militia alone could do the job, he said.

But something went wrong. General William Hull, a veteran of the Revolution, led his men to Canada. With his twenty-five thousand men he fell back to Detroit, where he soon surrendered to an inferior force of British and Indians. Niagara and Lake Champlain, the other two points of attack, remained in British hands. Definitely the war was not going well.

The country was divided. The old North and East were concerned over the failure of a war they had not wanted in the first place. Young America and the New West—the expansionists—could not win victory alone.

Meanwhile westerners decided that Governor William Henry Harrison, hero of Tippecanoe, was the man for the job. Time proved them right when he marched north in 1813 and recaptured Detroit. Commodore Oliver Hazard Perry won the Battle of Lake Erie and left the way free for Harrison to lead his men into Canada.

However, before these events took place, Americans were seeing dark days. During the summer of 1812, in the face of a discouraging campaign. Clay remained calm. He went up and down Kentucky wherever soldiers were assembling. He was the power behind the military power. There was even talk of placing him in command of all the western troops, but Clay knew his place was in Congress. The last days of 1812 found him there.

That month he had written to his good friend Caesar Rodney:

> . . . Mr. Madison is wholly unfit for the storms of war. . . . Admirably adapted to the tranquil scenes of peace . . . he is not fit for the rough and rude blasts which the conflicts of Nations generate.
>
> . . . I do not despair. The justness of our cause—the adequacy of our means to bring it to a successful issue—the spirit & patriotism of the country . . . will at last I think bring us honorably out.

The War Hawks felt themselves well adapted to the storms of war. Their first act in this Congress was to push the passage of a bill calling for twenty thousand more men to invade Canada.

Josiah Quincy of Massachusetts sprang to his feet to attack the bill. He lost no time in throwing down the gauntlet.

"I consider the invasion of Canada, as a means of carrying on this war, as *cruel, wanton, senseless and wicked,*" he thundered.

Even Captain Kidd and his buccaneers, he asserted, "had more apology for their deed than the American Cabinet." Looking contemptuously at Henry Clay in the Speaker's chair, he continued:

"Those must be very young politicians, their pinfeathers not yet grown—and however they may flutter on this floor, they are not yet fledged for any high or distant flight—who think that threats and appealing to fear are the ways of producing a disposition to negotiate in Great Britain or in any other nation which understands what it owes to its own safety and honor."

The war, fostered by Jefferson, Madison and Monroe, was part of a gigantic plot, he said. Jefferson, a Virginian, had been followed in the presidential chair by Madison, and James I would be succeeded by James II. James Monroe would be a dictator at the head of fifty-five thousand men.

Having made these charges, he took his seat amid the clamor and confusion of the House. Various members of the war party rose to defend their actions. But the Speaker's gavel did not descend. Henry Clay said nothing.

Then on January 8, 1813, two days later, he went into action. His speech continued for the better part of two days. The tall Kentuckian looked pale. Whether it was from indisposition or fury, none dared to say, but the Speaker's spirit was kindled to white heat. That much was evident.

He scoffed at Quincy's allusion to French influences and boldly asserted his nationalism.

"We have nothing to do with the affairs of Europe . . . except so far as these things affect the interest of our own country . . . we are too powerful for the mightiest nation in Europe, or all Europe combined. If we are separated and torn asunder, we shall become an easy prey to the weakest of them. In the latter dreadful contingency, our country will not be worth preserving."

He continued with a glowing tribute to Jefferson and a telling blow at the New England Confederacy, as dastardly a plot to secede from the Union as the one attributed to Aaron Burr.

Henry Clay was a born actor. In an age before the cinema and television, he exerted his histrionic charm to cast a spell over his audience. His present listeners were no exception.

Impressment alone, he declared, was reason enough to wage a war. We owed it to our "gallant tars" to fight a war and win it.

As to the invasion of Canada being wicked and unjustifiable, as his opponents claimed, Clay reminded his hearers:

"Canada innocent! Canada unoffending! Is it not in Canada that the tomahawk of the savage has been molded into

its deathlike form? Has it not been from Canadian maga-
zines, Malden and others, that those supplies have been
issued which nourish and continue the Indian hostilities—
supplies which have enabled the savage hordes to butcher
the garrison of Chicago, and to commit other horrible ex-
cesses and murders?"

The cold shadows of late afternoon were drifting in
through the long windows of the House of Representatives
as he finished his speech:

"We are told that England is a proud and lofty nation,
which, disdaining to wait for danger, meets it halfway.
Haughty as she is, we once triumphed over her, and if we
do not listen to the counsels of timidity and despair, we shall
again prevail. In such a cause, with the aid of Providence,
we must come out crowned with success; but if we fail, let
us fail like men, lash ourselves to our gallant tars, and expire
together in one common struggle, fighting for *free trade and
seamen's rights!*"

A roar of applause went up from his audience as he concluded. His leadership had turned the tide. His speech
aroused the country from its lethargy of doubt and despair.
He was indeed the Western Star. At last Congress was in the
mood for war.

But the war continued unpopular in the East in spite of
everything. New England continued to clamor for peace.
Her shipping interests were ruined. Unemployment was increasing. The costs of war were mounting.

When the Czar of Russia offered in March, 1813, to medi-
ate between the United States and Great Britain, Madison
accepted the offer without waiting to hear from Great Britain. Furthermore, he sent Secretary of the Treasury Albert
Gallatin and Senator James A. Bayard of Delaware to Europe
to join John Quincy Adams, American minister to Russia,
for the peace negotiations.

The British, however, turned down Russia's offer of medi-
ation. In November of the same year, they offered to negotiate directly with the United States. President Madison ac-

cepted, appointing Henry Clay and Jonathan Russell to serve with John Adams and James A. Bayard on the peace commission. Secretary of the Treasury Albert Gallatin, having previously failed to resign his post, was not eligible to be a member of the present commission. The resignation must come before he could join them.

With mixed emotions Henry Clay resigned his place as Speaker of the House of Representatives. He had felt a peculiar fondness for the chair ever since his fellow congressmen had placed him there on the occasion of his first day in the House. He had looked at it with longing when he was twice filling other men's unexpired terms in the Senate. The vigor, strength and drive of the lower house appealed to the young man far more than the prudence, caution and deliberation of the Senate members. Here in the House he had found his place. Here he belonged. Here he would gain fame, if fame were ever to be his.

So it was with some reluctance that he resigned the speakership. The task before him would be long and hard. England held the trump cards. In spite of Oliver Hazard Perry's victory on Lake Erie and General Harrison's triumph on the river Thames in Canada, the country to the north still dangled as a ripe plum before American eyes. If rumors were true, the net was closing on Napoleon in Europe. When England no longer had the French forces to deal with, she could turn her whole attention—and all her strength—toward America.

One cold day in January, 1814, Henry Clay faced President Madison across a table in the latter's private apartments.

"Mr. Clay, I have great confidence in your ability to outthink and outmaneuver the enemy," the President was saying in his usual clipped dry tones. "You will need both qualities in dealing with the British ministers."

Henry raised his head quickly to observe the meticulously groomed, aging figure of the man across from him. Was there possibly a gleam of humor in those cold sharp eyes? Could he be referring to the Speaker's well-known proclivity for cards, especially poker? Clay sighed. One might surmise but never be sure. The Chief Executive was pleasant enough at times, but he was about as communicative as the Sphinx.

"You will proceed at once to New York, where passage has been booked for you on the corvette *John Adams*. It will take you to Göteborg in Sweden, where the mission will meet," the President informed him. "Before you sail you will be joined by Mr. Jonathan Russell, a well-to-do merchant from Massachusetts. Mr. Christopher Hughes of Baltimore will also accompany you. He will act as secretary to the peace mission."

Clay nodded with satisfaction. "A most estimable young man. I am already acquainted with him."

"You will find passports for yourself and the others in your party awaiting you in New York," Mr. Madison said. He rose to his feet. "I wish you a safe journey, Mr. Clay. May you return with peace for our country."

"An honorable peace," Henry Clay amended gravely.

"To be sure," President Madison agreed. "An honorable peace."

11

MR. CLAY MEETS THE BRITISH

Henry Clay and Christopher Hughes were standing on the foredeck of the American warship *John Adams*. The spray was dashing against their faces as the ship rose and fell with the motion of the waves. Before them a gray expanse of sky and sea melted into one. The sun had not shone for several days.

"It has been a rough voyage," the younger man volunteered. "I'm glad I got my sea legs quickly."

Clay smiled. "The way ahead of us may be rougher. I'm referring to the work of the peace commission. There's a mountain of work ahead of us, Kit."

The other shrugged. "I expected that when I accepted the post of secretary. Tell me something about the other commissioners."

"Well, you know Jonathan Russell," his tall companion replied cautiously.

Christopher Hughes grinned. "I had ample time to learn while we were waiting all those days for him in New York so we could set sail. Massachusetts—rather serious—devoted to commerce and manufacturing—inclined to think of himself more highly than he ought to think—lacks the qualities of leadership—sometimes bitten by the green-eyed monster of jealousy."

Clay gave an amused smile. "You've painted a recognizable

picture, I think. Nevertheless Mr. Russell is one of our number and will make his contribution."

"Go on," Kit urged. "What about the others?"

"We'll start with John Quincy Adams," Henry Clay agreed. A slight grimace spread over his mobile features. "Son of old 'Alien and Sedition' Adams—attended school at Passy outside Paris when his father was commissioner to France in 1776—cold—ungracious at times—strictly Puritan— they say he reads five chapters of the Bible daily—forty-six years old—at present American minister at St. Petersburg."

Henry's blue eyes twinkled at the increasing stupefaction in the young secretary's face. "Don't underestimate Mr. Adams. If he thinks he is right—and he usually does—he will display a stubbornness and tenacity that will overshadow those qualities in the British commissioners, who will un- doubtedly be well supplied with them."

"And Bayard?" Hughes asked.

"A strong man," Clay answered promptly. "He is eager for peace. The President considered sending him to England on a peace mission before war broke out, but the plans did not materialize."

Young Hughes, observing the Kentuckian's enigmatic ex- pression, remembered the current rumor that Clay and the other War Hawks had blocked this move. Well, one thing was certain in Hughes' mind. He would rather have Henry Clay for him than against him.

"James Bayard is a Federalist from Delaware," Clay con- tinued. "He will be a powerful asset at the peace table. And to conclude, there is Albert Gallatin. He had not been for- mally appointed when we sailed, but that will be taken care of. It probably has been taken care of by now. He has been in Europe ever since Mr. Madison, hoping to make peace through Russian intervention, sent him there with Mr. Bayard. Mr. Gallatin neglected to resign as Secretary of the Treasury. That he must do before he can join us."

"He is foreign-born," Hughes commented.

"But a staunch American," Clay added quickly. "Born in

Switzerland fifty-three years ago—came to America in 1780—member of the House of Representatives from 1795 to 1801—Secretary of the Treasury since then—urbane, courteous, even-tempered—not at all like that pepper pot by the name of Clay from Kentucky."

"Henry Clay," Hughes said with a little smile, giving a hasty glance to be sure he was not overstepping the bounds of propriety. "Native Virginian—transplanted early to Kentucky—in politics since 1803—ardent Republican—Speaker of the House since 1811—leader of the war movement—"

" 'Mr. Clay's War' they call it in some quarters," the other said. There was a slight note of bitterness in his voice. "I wanted war no more than Grundy, Lowndes, Cheeves, Calhoun or Johnson. There simply was no other course. We were unwilling any longer to endure the galling insults of the British."

"—gallant gentleman—and valued friend," Kit finished with a look of admiration at the tall man who stood with his feet planted solidly on the deck as the sea wind blew in his face.

Henry Clay gave him a look of gratitude, and laid a hand on his companion's shoulder. "Thank you, Kit," he said earnestly. "It is good to know that you will be with me in the months ahead. There is a gigantic task before us. Peace will not come easily."

When the party docked in Sweden after a seven-week voyage, they were not met by Adams, Gallatin and Bayard as they had expected. The winter had been a severe one. Their ship dropped anchor twelve miles from Göteborg, and they were conducted by sledge to the city. There they half expected to find the other Americans, but they were disappointed. Because it was an era when communications were uncertain, the newly arrived commissioners cooled their heels for several weeks while they waited to hear from the others.

At last a message came from Gallatin and Bayard in London. Since Napoleon's defeat, which had occurred after Clay and his party had sailed from America, the British had decided that they would prefer London—or Ghent in the Netherlands—to Göteborg as a meeting place.

"This is pure insolence!" thirty-seven-year-old Henry Clay exclaimed hotly. "The British still think they are our masters and can treat us as they please."

He was convinced that the arbitrary change in plans was typical of British effrontery. He would never forget the fear behind the defiance in his mother's eyes when she protected her orphaned children from Tarleton's redcoats. So far as Clay was concerned, the British insults which led to the present war had only increased the scorn which he had for them. No, he would *not* go to London.

So the peace conference met at Ghent. It was early in July before all the American commissioners arrived there. Even then they had ample time to enjoy the hospitality of the quaint old city before the British representatives put in their appearance a month later.

At first the Americans were in no mood to indulge in social affairs, although they were glad to find time for them as the weeks passed by. For the present they rented an enormous house on the Rue des Champs and settled down to business.

The outlook was bad. Napoleon's defeat had left England with all her sea and land power to use against the United States. The news had come to Ghent that a mighty English armada was on its way across the Atlantic. One part would strike at Lake Champlain, one somewhere on the Atlantic and a third at New Orleans. The prospect was alarming, to say the least.

Soon after the British commissioners arrived, negotiations got under way. At first, affairs seemed at an impasse. The Americans wanted an end to impressment; a clear statement of neutral rights (in case of any future wars); payment for property damage; and (if possible) Canada. On the other hand, the British demanded the Northwest Territory as a "buffer state"; a clear definition of the Canadian border with a part of Maine included in British territory; the sole right to maintain armed forces on the Great Lakes; and the continued right to navigation on the Mississippi River.

For a time neither side would yield an inch. Meetings that lasted for hours resulted in long periods of waiting while couriers went to London to get further instructions for the British commissioners.

Meanwhile tempers wore thin in the house on the Rue des Champs. John Quincy Adams, reared in a strict New England tradition, looked askance at Mr. Clay and his mode of living.

Indefatigable Henry Clay could wrangle all day at the conference table, dress for dinner, enjoy to the fullest the European foods, wines and "segars," declare a truce, play cards with the Englishmen until night turned to day, and then appear again at the conference table ready for another verbal battle.

The man from Massachusetts eyed him coldly one day. "Mr. Clay, I scarcely see how you can do your duty by your country. Usually when I am rising—to read my daily five chapters in the Bible," he added with a touch of asperity— "I see your lights going out across the courtyard."

Mr. Clay rolled between his lips with relish one of the cigars for which John Adams had conceived such a violent hatred. He could not resist this opportunity to needle the senior statesman.

"Evidently you do not take your cards seriously, Mr. Adams."

The New England man winced. Only the day before, in a slow-moving game of whist, Clay had won from him a hand-painted flower picture which had fallen to the latter in a lottery.

"Our British opponents are past masters at bluffing," Clay continued. "Well, I know something of that art, too. At the card table a lifted eyebrow, a change of tone, a betraying gesture—all tell their story. If I can learn their tricks at cards, perhaps I can outguess them at the council table."

For a moment John Adams looked at him with respect. "Are you serious, sir?"

The Kentuckian's eyes twinkled. "Some say I am; some say I'm not. But I'll tell you this, Mr. Adams. I enjoy life thoroughly."

All the Americans enjoyed life, each in his own fashion. The Intendant, the Mayor and the leading citizens often invited them to dinner. Gallatin and his sixteen-year-old son, who was serving as his father's secretary, attended the French theater every night. Adams allowed himself a weekly trip there. Gallatin, Adams and Bayard were invited to join the Society of Fine Arts and Letters. Clay, Russell and Hughes received invitations to the Society of Agriculture and Botany.

So the long, weary days passed until October when the commission was further disheartened by the news that the British had seized Washington and burned the Capitol and the White House. Not long after that, Clay received personal letters from home that told him Lucretia, who had been in Washington when he sailed, was safe at Ashland.

"Thank God for that!" he said fervently. A broad smile crossed his face as he read on. "So Dolley Madison drove out of Washington with Peale's portrait of Washington and a sheaf of important state papers in her carriage right in the face of the enemy. That's just like her—all fire and daring and mettle. Too bad she can't defy the British over the peace table. It's a pity her husband can't catch some of her spirit."

One day Lord Goulburn from British headquarters sent Clay a London newspaper with an account of the burning of Washington. With it came a polite note expressing the writer's regret at sending such an unpleasant report, but he was sure Mr. Clay would like to have the latest news.

Henry Clay reciprocated soon after with a Paris newspaper containing news of American naval victories that followed the burning of Washington. He was sorry, he said, to give such a disconcerting report, but he was certain the English commissioner would wish to be informed.

Diplomatic progress between the two nations seemed to be at a standstill. The British would not yield. All the American commissioners except Henry Clay began to adopt a conciliatory mood.

"No!" he cried angrily. "They are bluffing. Let them guess what we will do. Keep them talking. We will finally wear them down."

He was right. In spite of the British commissioners' haughty, superior air, Great Britain was looking toward peace. Her subjects were weary of war. They were tired of the taxes they had paid for more than twelve years. America was far away. Although they did not acknowledge it, they were eager to make peace.

"Wait for the Battle of New Orleans!" Clay pleaded. "If we win there, *we* will dictate the terms."

"We are outnumbered three to one in the field," Adams informed him in his dry-as-dust voice.

Gallatin added, "If we lose at New Orleans, we will not be as well off as we now are."

"Wait!" Clay begged. "We may yet dictate the terms."

But the other commissioners saw no point in waiting. The Treaty of Ghent was signed on December 24, 1814, at the Convent of the Chartreaux, where the British had their headquarters. It was a treaty which brought a peace with some semblance of honor to each nation. The two countries returned to prewar conditions. Impressment, no longer an issue now that England had ceased to wage war with France, was not mentioned. Other matters were referred to committees. Clay, Adams and Gallatin were to meet later with British commissioners in London to make a commercial treaty.

Messengers were impatient to take the news to their respective countries. The British secretary ordered his carriage and rattled off at once over the cobblestones of the city. Christopher Hughes fumed at the delay, but he was forced to wait until John Quincy Adams wrote a dispatch to the President of the United States. The letter was finally ready.

"But this does not mention my name," the young secretary said, flushing angrily as he scanned the open sheet.

"It is customary to name only the principals, Mr. Hughes," John Adams told him in his nasal New England twang. "I confess you have done your work well. I shall commend you in a later communication, sir."

When Christopher Hughes sat down to dinner later with the commissioners, who were dining by invitation in a private home, Henry Clay noted that the secretary's face was perplexed and troubled.

Under the pretense of giving him further instructions, Clay led him out to the balcony. Impulsively he threw an arm about the younger man's shoulders.

"Something is wrong, Kit. What is it?"

Hughes turned to him in the moonlight. The kindly understanding in Clay's face prompted him to pour out his grievances in a sudden spate of words. When he had finished, Clay lost no time in applying balm to his wounded feelings.

"Believe me, my dear fellow, I can sympathize with you. Mr. Adams sometimes rubs me the wrong way, too. I'm not sure he doesn't do it purposely. There's no love lost between us, I assure you. But our work is done and the treaty is completed. Your services have helped to complete the job. Indeed, you should have been mentioned. If I had been responsible for the drafting of the letter, you would have been. But Old Surly, as I've heard you call him, is a stickler for rules and propriety. And, in truth, your most valuable contribution could not be noted. As a secretary you were invaluable, but as a man you were superb. Your laughter, your gaiety, your sense of humor—they made existence a joy and a delight in spite of Mr. Adams' irascibility."

There were tears in the young secretary's eyes as he clasped Henry Clay's outstretched hand. "I shall never forget those words, sir."

On January 7, 1815, Clay left for Paris. There he visited his friend William H. Crawford, American minister to France. While in the French capital Clay was presented to

Louis XVIII. He also met Lord Wellington, whom he greatly admired. The days passed and still he remained in the city on the Seine.

At last the long-expected news of the Battle of New Orleans arrived. General Andrew Jackson had led the Americans to victory over a vastly superior number of troops under General Pakenham. The power of Great Britain over America was broken at last. If only the peace treaty could have been postponed—

But Henry Clay lost no time in indulging in vain regrets. "Hurrah!" he cried in almost boyish abandon. "This should prove something about America to the whole world."

He set out immediately for London. Now he could look the haughty Britons in the eye. Something strange had happened to him. He no longer felt any animosity toward them. For three months he was entertained by a friendly people. He met Sir Walter Scott, the literary lion of the hour. He did his part in making a commercial treaty. Then, leaving John Quincy Adams to finish the work, as they had previously agreed, he went to New York, where he attended a large public dinner in his honor. At last he turned his face toward home. It was September when he arrived in Kentucky to be united with his family at Ashland, where the leaves were beginning to turn red and gold.

12

A MAN OF THE AMERICAS

IT WAS OCTOBER, 1815. HENRY CLAY, HOME AT LAST AFTER his long absence in Europe, paced back and forth in the morning room at Ashland. Lucretia was sitting in a small rocking chair, working on some embroidery, and the golden autumn sunshine drifting in at the long open windows bathed her in a mellow aura. Out on the lawn he could hear the shouts of their children at play.

"Kentucky is the most beautiful of our eighteen states and Ashland is the choice spot in it," he declared feelingly. "Old John Marshall was right when he said Kentucky is a heaven of a place."

Lucretia smiled. None knew better than she that her husband had much of the small boy in him in spite of his dignified demeanor. When he was enthusiastic, every other remark was punctuated with superlatives.

"I often thought so when I was far away in Washington," she replied simply.

Henry looked at her quickly. He thrived on the atmosphere of the capital with its gay society, its colorful levees, balls and receptions. Most of all, he enjoyed the political activities in the Senate and House of Representatives as well as in the private rooms where momentous issues were frequently decided behind closed doors. While he loved the bustle and excitement, he knew that Lucretia was truly at home only in the peaceful tranquillity of Ashland. Was she unhappy as the wife of Henry Clay, who was as well known in Washington as in Lexington?

He scanned her placid face, and to his relief saw no trace of regret. Unaware of his gaze, she continued to thrust the needle in and out of the silken material in her slim white hands.

He looked beyond her into the drawing room. His eyes lighted up. "Do you like the gold-brocaded draperies?" he asked eagerly. "They were the finest I could buy in Lyons."

"Indeed I do," she assured him. "They are exquisite. And the Madame Récamier sofas as well. Your taste is perfect, my dear."

"And you are pleased with your watch?" he asked, sitting down beside her to examine the little bauble of gold and pearls pinned on the front of her gown.

"Almost as much as I am with the giver," she said with a little smile.

"It's not good enough for you," he sighed. "I couldn't find anything that was. You deserve a diadem or a tiara or something of the sort. It's hard for you to be dragged back and forth over miserable roads to Washington all the time with those lively youngsters."

"When we go again, I hope we can make better arrangements for Theodore and Thomas," she told him. A little frown appeared between her eyes. "Apparently that school down in the country was poorly managed. They were like young wildcats when I came home from Washington. I don't know how I should have managed without that nice Mr. Kendall whom I engaged as their tutor. He came to my rescue and took them over when they really needed a man. By the way, I understand he is still in Lexington."

"I must extend my hearty thanks to him," her husband said. "I fear our boys have sometimes lacked a father's firm hand."

Late in 1815 the Clay family set out for Washington. Lucretia would have preferred to remain at home with the

children, but Henry wanted them all with him. He had
already been separated too long from his family.

Immediately upon his return to Congress he was re-
elected Speaker of the House of Representatives. This act
on the part of his colleagues he accepted gratefully, for he
had relinquished the post with regret more than a year ago
when he had been appointed to the peace commission.

With the other "Young Republicans," as the younger
Democratic-Republicans now called themselves, he set
about building a strong America. This was his dream, his
passion, his first thought on awaking, his last before dropping off to sleep. He had definite ideas on how this should
be achieved, and many times while he was Speaker he resigned his seat temporarily and came down onto the floor.

He had done this on a day in January, 1816. Lucretia in
her usual balcony seat thought she had never seen him look
so ardent, so eager, so glowing. How often he had spoken
to her in private of his hopes for the New America! Now
he was declaiming those same sentiments from the floor of
the House.

"I love true glory," he declared. "It is the sentiment
which ought to be cherished; and in spite of cavils and
sneers and attempts to put it down, it will finally conduct
this nation to that height to which God and nature have
destined it."

He wanted to increase the Army and the Navy. He
wanted America to be self-sufficient. He had said virtually
the same thing in 1809 in the Kentucky legislature when
he introduced his "homespun bill." Now that more fac-
tories had been started at home during the war with England, their products must be protected by a high tariff
from competition with English and European goods that
were once more flowing into the country. He wanted "internal improvements." In other words, better communications. No one knew better than a westerner how mud-
clogged roads could stifle and strangle trade and commerce. If it were not for the Mississippi, Kentucky would

be almost cut off from eastern markets. And finally he wanted a strong national bank in order to finance these improvements.

His January speech was the foundation of the American system, which all his life was as near to the statesman from Kentucky as eating or breathing.

But his message was not solely concerned with domestic matters. He wanted aid from the United States government for the South American peoples who were rising against the bonds of Spain. Love of freedom was an integral part of Clay's nature. It asserted itself in his intense patriotism and again in his stand on Emancipation, a gradual freeing of the Negro slaves. Also he had learned much about the intricacies of foreign diplomacy when he was in Europe. He had seen Napoleon's rise and subsequent success threaten to engulf Europe and Great Britain. Since the days of Ghent he had watched the great powers of Europe as they took a common reactionary stand against popular liberties. He knew that Spain—with the help of her allies— could stifle the newborn voice of freedom in South America, which had begun with Venezuela's declaration of freedom in 1811. And if a foreign stranglehold were exercised there, who could say how fast and how far it would extend northward? After all, the United States had felt the ruthless hand of Spain more than once, as Kentuckians—for whom the Mississippi was the lifeline of trade and commerce— could testify.

As usual, Clay was ahead of his times. While the United States had offered a token sympathy to Venezuela in her struggle, the American government had taken no practical steps to give aid to her neighbor to the south.

"I consider the release of any part of America from the dominions of the Old World as adding to the general security of the New," he proclaimed. With a sympathetic light breaking over his impassioned features, he continued, "I cannot contemplate the exertions of the people of South

America without wishing that they might triumph and nobly triumph!"

But he was almost alone in his wish. The people and the government of the United States seemed to feel that South America was far removed from them. For many years the main stream of their trade and commerce had flowed back and forth across the Atlantic except for imports of rum, sugar and molasses from the West Indies. As a national figure, Henry Clay stood almost alone in his feeling for and understanding of the Latin American countries.

Meanwhile President Madison offered him the post of Secretary of War. Clay courteously declined and saw the position fall to James Monroe. When Monroe became president in 1817, he, too, tried to place the Kentuckian in his cabinet in the same capacity. Again Clay declined. He refused also to become Minister to England as earlier he had refused to become Minister to Russia.

The fact was that he held already the place nearest his heart—the Speaker of the House. Since 1811 he had wielded the gavel here except for the interval when he was away at Ghent. Here was everything for which he could ask. Excitement, action, challenge, statesmanship—and all the while he could feel the throbbing pulse of a growing nation. Here he belonged and here, if it pleased Providence, he would stay.

He was certain that as Speaker of the House he could aid South America more than he could have done in the President's cabinet. John Quincy Adams, Secretary of State under President Monroe, was proceeding cautiously. Besides being a product of New England, he had an easterner's view of what was good for the country. Democratic government in South America he dismissed as a quixotic dream, saying that it was foolhardy for us to have any entangling alliances with those fledgling nations.

Alone with Lucretia in their Washington house, Clay unleashed his pent-up feelings. She watched him with concern as he paced back and forth across the hearthrug until she wondered if he would wear it to shreds.

Suddenly he stopped short and eyed her sternly. His hands were thrust deep into his pockets. "How can our government be so blind?" he demanded. "Mr. Adams apparently believes the borders of the United States end at Boston, and Mr. Monroe listens to him. I cannot understand the President. He is a man of great ability and yet—"

"South America seems so far away," Lucretia said with a small sigh. "People know so little about Venezuela and those other countries you are always talking about."

Henry gave a snort of disgust. "Then I shall keep informing them. Do you know what John Quincy Adams said about me the other day? 'Mr. Clay has mounted his South American hobby horse.' What do you think of that? The old rascal hasn't improved since Ghent days."

In 1818 Henry Clay told Congress, "South America is about five thousand miles in length, and in some places nearly three thousand in breadth. Within this vast region we behold the most sublime and interesting objects of creation: the loftiest mountains, the most majestic rivers in the world; the richest mines of the precious metals and the choicest productions of the earth. We behold there a spectacle still more interesting and sublime—the glorious spectacle of eighteen millions of people struggling to burst their chains and be free."

Apparently Henry Clay had the faculty for placing himself in others' shoes. He could and did imagine the sufferings of these people who were still struggling to break the bonds that had held them for generations. His feeling of kinship with these people of another race shone through his words:

"Whenever I think of Spanish America, the image irresistibly forces itself upon my mind of an elder brother whose education has been neglected, whose person has been abused and maltreated, and who has been disinherited by the unkindness of an unnatural parent. And when I contemplate the glorious struggle which that country is now making, I think I behold that brother rising, by the power and energy of his fine native genius, to the manly rank which nature and nature's God intended for him."

Clay continued to plead for recognition of the South American countries. The administration continued to turn a deaf ear. But freedom was obtaining a foothold in South America. La Plata, Argentina, had been independent since Chile became free in 1817. And Colombia followed her sister republic in 1819.

Again Henry Clay's voice was heard:

"What would I give could we appreciate the advantages which may be realized by our pursuing the course which I propose! It is in our power to create a system of which we shall be the center, and in which all South America will act with us. In respect to commerce, we should be most benefited; this country would become the place of deposit of the commerce of the world. . . . We should become the center of a system which would constitute the rallying point of human wisdom against all the despotism of the Old World. . . . Our institutions now make us free; but how long shall we continue so, if we mold our opinions on those of Europe? Let us break these commercial and political fetters; let us no longer watch the nod of any European politician, let us become real and true Americans, and place ourselves at the head of the American system."

His words at last turned the tide. On February 10, 1821, he presented a resolution which said that the House of Representatives participated with the people of the United States in their sympathy for the South Americans; and it was ready to support the President whenever he saw fit to recognize their governments. The resolution passed and a committee, headed by the Speaker, laid it before the President.

The deed was done. Through Henry Clay's unceasing efforts, the United States was first among the nations of the world to recognize the South American republics and to extend to them the hand of friendship.

His work did not go unappreciated by South Americans. His speeches were translated into Spanish and read all over South America. The very mention of his name brought wild applause.

More than a century later his statue was given a place of honor in the city of Caracas, the capital of Venezuela. Copies were placed in other South American cities. Even in the twentieth century, as an apostle of good will and a champion of freedom, Henry Clay wields an influence in South America as well as in his native land.

13

THE MISSOURI COMPROMISE

THE TIME WAS LATE 1818. THE CLAYS WERE AGAIN IN Washington for the opening of Congress. The session gave promise of being a stormy one. Lucretia knew all the signs. Henry left the house early in the morning and returned late at night. Nevertheless, frequent visitors knocked at the front door after the evening meal and were admitted into her husband's study where she could hear the murmur of their voices long after she had retired.

But tonight belonged by some lucky accident to her husband and herself alone. The children had been in bed for an hour. No politicians had disturbed the quiet of the peaceful parlor. Clay held his long, slim hands up to the glowing flames on the hearth.

"Appearances are deceptive," he observed with a smile. "You and I might be a farmer and his wife in some secluded spot of Kentucky instead of a congressman and his lady in the heart of the nation's capital."

"And you would be utterly miserable," Lucretia returned.

Clay laughed. "How well you know me! I have served under three presidents—Jefferson, Madison and now Monroe. I have come to feel that I belong here."

Lucretia's knitting dropped into her lap. "Don't you think I should know you after being married to you for

125

nearly twenty years? You would never be happy anywhere but in the House unless—"

"Unless what, 'Cretia?"

She had almost said: "Unless you were in the President's chair."

That could wait. She was sure he had included it in his plans, but the words must come from him. And why not? The name of Henry Clay should unlock any door.

Her husband had already forgotten his question. He was staring absorbedly into the flames.

"A penny for your thoughts," Lucretia offered.

Henry gave a start. "I was thinking of the positions I might have filled. I do not regret in the least not becoming Secretary of War or minister to England last year when Mr. Monroe approached me. No, I rejoice in the post of Speaker of the House. It is the most exciting career I know of except—"

He broke off in the middle of a sentence. Lucretia was positive now that he was thinking of the presidency. She recognized his ambition, but it was difficult for her in her woman's world to follow him into the realm of national problems. Nevertheless, she made the attempt.

"Missouri will apply early in the session for statehood, will she not?" she inquired.

Her husband nodded. "That will be the main business. But first we must attend to General Andrew Jackson."

Clay might have added with perfect truth, "—and President Monroe."

He had never quite forgiven the President for not making him Secretary of State. The post was tendered instead to John Quincy Adams, for whom the Kentuckian had held no love since Ghent days. When the posts of Secretary of War and Minister to England had been offered Harry of the West, as Clay had been known since his early rise to national fame, he had refused them scornfully and chosen to remain the Speaker of the House. In that post he felt that he had a finger upon the pulse of the infant nation that by leaps and strides was becoming a giant.

Now, across the hearth from Lucretia in their Washington home, forty-two-year-old Henry Clay felt a somewhat understandable satisfaction in attacking the Chief of State through his officer Andrew Jackson. After all, President Monroe was supposed to be Commander-in-Chief of the Army. If he had made his power felt, Jackson would never have dared—

The Kentuckian flexed his fingers in the firelight. The shadows cast by the flames played upon his earnest face.

"I confess I have no love for Jackson," he admitted. "How could I after he accused Kentuckians at the Battle of New Orleans of being cowards? After all, most of the poor fellows possessed only sticks, stones and knives in place of muskets. One could hardly expect them to advance in the face of the enemy with such weapons. And the few Kentuckians who had rifles—such as Ephraim Brank—proved themselves sharpshooters of the first order."

"Kentuckians can hardly be accused of cowardice," Lucretia agreed. "Perhaps it was a mistake on Jackson's part."

"A great mistake," Clay agreed grimly, "but not half so great a mistake as the recent Indian affair in the Floridas. With or without benefit of orders from the War Department, the invincible Andrew plunged into the section, routed the Indians and captured two British subjects who he said were allies of the Indians. Then he hanged the Indian chiefs and shot the Britishers. After he had occupied Pensacola for a time, he left it under military guard and led his army out of Spanish territory back to American soil. From the reception he received in the Southeast you would think he had returned from Hell itself. Meanwhile the Spanish minister is protesting to our government loud enough to be heard above the huzzas of the populace in Alabama and Georgia. It's quite a mess to straighten out. Do we reward or punish him?"

"You will know what to do when the time comes,"
Lucretia said simply. "I am sure you will."

Clay gave a short laugh. "I wish I were as certain as you
are. Old Hickory is not an easy man to handle. The Florida
Indians will testify to that. And now our government seems
in a mood to excuse—even to praise—him."

The next day in the House, the Speaker came down from
the chair and spoke his mind frankly and freely. He condemned the harsh treaty which Jackson had forced on the
Creek Indians in 1814. He deplored the treatment of the
Indian chiefs who had been captured by trickery and then
hanged. He denounced as murder the execution of the
Englishmen.

"Remember that Greece had her Alexander, Rome her
Caesar, England her Cromwell, France her Bonaparte; if
we would escape the rock on which they split we must
avoid their errors," he warned.

He had thrown down the gauntlet. Andrew Jackson never
forgave him. If the long shadow of slavery was beginning to
creep across the United States, perhaps the shadow of Old
Hickory was beginning to engulf the man whom his
admirers called the Western Star.

But there was something of greater import in the Fifteenth
Congress than the question of Andrew Jackson. Missouri,
far away on the western frontier, was asking for admission
to the Union. Originally a part of the Louisiana Purchase,
the Missouri Territory allowed slavery. In 1819 there were
eleven slave states and eleven free states in the Union.
What of Missouri? Should she be admitted as a slave state?
The slavery issue which had been present ever since George
Washington's day was threatening the peace of the nation.

Henry Clay, who loved the Union even more than he
hated slavery, watched the approaching storm with dread.
With a sinking heart he read what old Thomas Jefferson had
written from his Virginia mountaintop:

I have for a long time ceased to pay attention to public affairs, content to be a passenger in our bark to the shore from which I am not far distant. But this . . . issue, like a fire bell in the night, awakened and filled me with terror. I considered it once as the knell of the Union. It hushed, indeed for the moment, but this is a delay only, not a final sentence. It is my only . . . comfort that I will not live to see the country rent apart, and this glorious experiment in self-government made useless.

Almost as soon as the Fifteenth Congress opened, James Tallmadge of New York proposed an amendment to Missouri's Enabling Act, prohibiting the further introduction of slaves into Missouri and freeing, at twenty-five, all slave children born in the state.

Hot with anger, Howell Cobb from Georgia shouted at Representative Tallmadge: "If you persist, the Union will be dissolved. You have kindled a fire which all the waters of the ocean cannot put out, which seas of blood can only extinguish."

Mr. Tallmadge's reply was quick in coming. "If the dissolution of the Union must take place, let it be so! If civil war, which gentlemen so threaten, must come, I can only say, let it come!"

The "fire bell in the night" was clanging. There had been in the past a tacit agreement that the Ohio River was the boundary line between the free states and the slave states, but that agreement was a thing of the past. The matter had come to a head, and slavery limits must be more clearly defined, for the frontier was pushing westward.

All during that session of Congress the question of Missouri was discussed, argued and debated. The eleven slave states opposed Tallmadge's proposal; the eleven free states supported it. When Congress closed its doors for the summer, the problem was still undecided. For the time being, Missouri was not admitted.

That summer down in Kentucky Henry Clay searched his soul. Because he was an astute politician as well as an earnest man he listened to the opinions of all with whom he came in contact. They ranged from Bluegrass aristocracy to the slaves themselves.

Most Lexingtonians of means—in fact, most Kentuckians—were for slavery. They were eager to admit Missouri as a slave state, but there was a rock-ribbed minority even in Kentucky who insisted with adamantine firmness that Missouri must be free. Neither side would yield an inch.

One night, after his usual game of cards, Clay left the Phoenix Hotel, which had earlier been called Postlethwaite's Tavern, and strolled westward on Main Street instead of ordering his horse and riding to Ashland. The hour was late and all the places of business were closed. Only a few pedestrians were abroad. In the distance a single carriage rolled away.

The statesman walked along deep in thought. He looked up with a start as he reached Cheapside. The public auction block loomed up in the moonlight. In fancy he could hear the chant of the auctioneer as he displayed his human wares: "How much am I bid, gentlemen, for this likely-looking wench? Ninety dollars—who will give me ninety-five?—going—going—"

How many times had Henry Clay seen cringing mulatto slave girls displayed thus to a callous public? How many times had he passed the slave coops a few blocks away where a conglomerate mass of suffering, miserable black humanity was kept until it was marketed like cattle? How many times had he been aware of slave cordons, roped like animals, passing by Ashland toward Lexington, usually in the dead of night to spare the sensibilities of white citizens who might feel qualms at the sight of so much dirt, disease and degradation?

"God!" he exclaimed passionately, clasping his hands together. "If only a man could live up to his ideals and share them with others."

Long ago he had decided what would be the fate of his

own slaves when he passed from the scene of the living. By then his sons would be the heads of their own establishments. His daughters would be married. There would be enough and to spare for Lucretia if she survived him. There was the land—always the land. If his children could not divide it satisfactorily and profitably, then it could be sold and the proceeds distributed among them. But first his slaves—the black members of his family, he reflected with a twisted smile—must be emancipated and provided with the means to go to faraway Africa and newly established Liberia. Then at last he could rest in his grave in peace, for slavery went strongly against the grain with the master of Ashland.

"What would I not give to free them now?" he muttered. "But I have a growing family to support. It would be a grievous thing to turn those ignorant, gullible, childlike people loose in a cruel world. They would starve or turn to crime in less than a twelvemonth. Clearly that course is impossible. No, Emancipation is the answer, not Abolition. Furthermore, I cannot strip my own flesh and blood to subsidize my blacks. Their freedom must wait awhile. I simply must compromise my ideals for the time being."

Compromise! The North could not sweep the nation into its way of thinking. The South could not demand all and give nothing. There must be a way that was pleasing to both sides. Clay shuddered as he remembered certain words that had been bandied about in the last Congress. *Secession. Civil war. Disunion.* Such thoughts were wicked and unthinkable. Surely there was a way out of the dilemma.

It was December, 1819. The Sixteenth Congress had assembled. Missouri was still seeking admission to the Union with, it seemed, as little chance for success as last year. Congress seemed deadlocked on the matter. Meanwhile a bill admitting Maine, a territory of Massachusetts, as a free state had passed the House and was waiting for action in the Senate.

When the Missouri bill with its amendment (proposed by

John W. Taylor of New York this time) came up in the House, it was passed and sent to the Senate. The Senate struck out the amendment, attached the bill to that admitting Maine, then passed the amended Maine bill.

The House refused to accept the proposal. Tempers grew hotter and words more bitter day by day. Congress had reached a stalemate, as had been expected.

Everyone in the United States knew Mr. Clay's stand on slavery. In 1816 he had presided at the organization meeting in Washington of the American Colonization Society, a group of persons whose purpose was to emancipate gradually all slaves and send them back to Africa. But Henry Clay was a practical man. Through inheritance and the force of circumstance he owned house servants and field hands. In the first half of the nineteenth century in the South it was virtually impossible for a man of property to escape such a situation. He was caught in the web of an institution which he might condemn, but with which he must live. The solution of the problem must come gradually. Meanwhile life must be lived from day to day.

The people in the Missouri Territory—mostly southerners —already owned slaves. If these slaves were freed, the slaveholders would be bankrupt. Even if they were allowed to keep them, and still slavery was henceforth barred from Missouri, no slaveholders would wish to settle there. Why should the North be allowed to dictate how Missouri would come into the nation?

On February 3, 1820, "the great Mr. Clay" rose in the House to speak on the Missouri question. The Senate had adjourned so that the senators might listen. Indeed it seemed as though all Washington had turned out to hear him. The galleries were filled and the spectators overflowed on the floor of the semicircular chamber.

"I am opposed to slavery," Clay told his audience. "If I were a citizen of Missouri, I would strenuously oppose any further introduction of slaves into my state; I would try to make some provision to emancipate those already there.

But I am not a citizen of Missouri and I have no right to force her to adopt my opinions, especially as she is unrepresented here."

Missouri had the constitutional right to come into the Union as she chose, he concluded. He merely wanted justice done.

At the end of his four-hour speech darkness had fallen and the room was ablaze with candles. His audience had hardly stirred, so intent were they on his words. As he finished, they thronged forward to congratulate him upon his speech.

But in spite of the speech Missouri remained outside the Union. Clay's oratory had not broken the deadlock. Neither side would yield an inch.

In the seclusion of their home one night Henry discussed the matter with his wife. "It seems ridiculous," he said soberly. "What does it really matter whether Missouri is a slave or a free state? I know slavery is evil, but the unity of the country is the paramount issue. Given time, slavery will wear itself out; but we must be one nation, not several sections."

Lucretia raised her delicate eyebrows. "Mr. John Randolph does not agree with you."

Henry gave an impatient exclamation. "I believe he would deliver the Union over to destruction if he thought it benefited the South—especially Virginia. How can a man be so blind? Sometimes I think he is demented."

"He will never change," Lucretia prophesied.

Henry's eyes gleamed. "He won't change, but some other members of the House may. I heard something very interesting today, 'Cretia—by way of the grapevine."

His wife laid down her embroidery. She was no political scholar but she was the wife of Henry Clay, and she loved to watch the play of his finely molded, mobile features as he talked his way through a problem. He was doing that now.

"Senator Thomas of Illinois will soon present an amendment to Missouri's request for statehood. I was fortunate enough to secure an advance copy. It read like this:

And be it further enacted, That in all that territory ceded by France to the United States, under the name of Louisiana, which lies north of thirty-six degrees thirty minutes north latitude, excepting only such part thereof as is included within the limits of the State contemplated by this act, slavery and involuntary servitude, otherwise than in the punishment of crimes whereof the party shall have been duly convicted, shall be and is hereby forever prohibited."

His wife rolled her eyes in mock despair. "Please translate!"

Clay's eyes twinkled. "In everyday language, Senator Thomas is proposing that Missouri be admitted as a slave state and Maine as a free state. That should please the South. Also it will keep the balance between slave and free states. To continue, the southern boundary of Missouri shall be the northern border—except for Missouri—of slavery in the Louisiana Purchase. Beyond that line the land shall be forever free."

"It doesn't really settle anything, Henry," Lucretia objected. "It's only a compromise."

"Of course it's a compromise," he agreed. "A compromise that will save the Union. As I've said before, time will solve the slavery question in one way or another, but the Union must be preserved right now. It sounds like a good idea. I shall support Thomas."

Soon the senator from Illinois presented his amendment to Missouri's bid for statehood. By now it had come to be known as the Missouri Compromise. It was debated in the House furiously and bitterly. John Randolph and his fellow secessionists stood out against it to the end. Speaker Clay used all his influence for it.

At last it came to a vote on March 2, 1820. The result was almost a tie—90 to 87 in favor of the measure. Henry Clay gave a sigh of relief. He had used all his powers of persuasion openly and in private to secure the passage of the bill.

His triumph was short-lived. Early next morning cantankerous old John Randolph rose to his feet in the House of Representatives.

"Mr. Speaker!" he snarled. "I move that the vote on the Missouri Compromise be reconsidered!"

Clay felt as though he had been doused with ice water. In the rush of business yesterday he had failed to send the bill to the Senate. He knew that some politicians who had voted for the Compromise might change their minds if there were a recount. The Speaker thought quickly. Without changing his expression he gravely answered the Virginian.

"The motion to reconsider is not in order. It will not be entertained until the routine business of the House is finished."

Randolph had to be satisfied with this decision. He fumed and fretted while various petitions and bills came up for consideration. As the business of the day proceeded, Clay signed the Compromise Bill and handed it to the House clerk. The Speaker acted so quietly that his action went unnoticed. No one but the clerk was the wiser.

At last John Randolph rose once more to his feet. "I demand a recount," he said in his high falsetto voice.

From the Speaker's chair Clay gave him a long, level look. There was the assurance of victory on his face.

"The bill has gone to the Senate, Mr. Randolph," he informed him. "There is no longer an opportunity for reconsideration."

Randolph was beside himself with rage. Henry Clay had outwitted him and, in so doing, had made one more enemy. He would make many enemies during the course of his long life.

The threat of secession was over for the time. The Senate was satisfied with the Compromise and soon passed it. The ship of state still sailed. Henry Clay had achieved what he wanted more than anything else in the world—even more than the presidency.

The Union had been preserved!

From this time on, the press began to refer to Henry Clay as "The Great Compromiser" or "The Great Pacificator." At public dinners a favorite toast was "Henry Clay: Our Next President!"

Meanwhile Congress adjourned. The Clays returned home. That winter Henry went back to Washington alone. By now the campaign for the presidency was well along. Other names, too, had been mentioned. John Quincy Adams, Secretary of State. William H. Crawford, Secretary of the Treasury and General Andrew Jackson, hero of the Battle of New Orleans.

Down in Kentucky a flock of young Clays perused every newspaper that came to the house. There was no doubt in their minds as to who would make the best president. Nor was there in the mind of their gentle, sweet-faced mother.

Now it was the spring of 1821 in Kentucky. The master of Ashland was returning home at last. This time he did not intend to run for re-election to Congress. There were several reasons for this decision. He mentioned them to his friends and acquaintances. During his many absences the house and the farm had run down. Ashland must be restored. There were debts which he must pay. He had generously gone on a friend's note. The friend had then failed in business, leaving Clay with a sizable debt to the Bank of the United States. Then he must earn money for an increasingly expensive family, which had been swelled by James Brown Clay and John Morrison Clay within the last few years. (Baby Laura had scarcely opened her eyes on the world in 1816 before she closed them again.)

But the former Speaker of the House did not voice the main reason for his return. He must mend his political fences in preparation for the coming presidential race. And the brightest side of the picture was that he would be once more at home with his wife and children. For a time, at least, he could renew his strength at Ashland, whose hearth flames always shone bright in his heart, no matter how many miles lay between them and him.

14

HENRY CLAY FIGHTS
A SECOND DUEL

HENRY CLAY WAS BACK AT ASHLAND. THE QUIET, DIGNIFIED beauty of the Georgian house on its four-hundred-acre tract of land brought balm to the heart of a weary man. When he was not in court or at his law office, he was riding over the farm or inspecting his livestock.

Under his supervision the house was painted inside and out, the gardens weeded, the borders lined. Each morning in the small office at the left of the wide entrance hall he met the overseer and went over the plans for the day.

By midsummer much of the former beauty of Ashland was restored. One day in June, Henry found himself in the solitude of his octagonal-shaped, walnut-paneled library where a subdued light sifted in through the skylight. He could hear the hum of the servants' voices somewhere in the rear of the house. He knew Lucretia and Eliza were with their mother in the dairy house on the west slope. The butter and eggs which the mistress of Ashland supplied weekly to the Phoenix Hotel in Lexington were her especial pride.

Clay laid aside the Lexington *Intelligencer*. Books and newspapers never held his interest for long. He was always too occupied with turning over in his mind plans for action.

A few minutes later he strolled out the front door in search of his wife. Frankly he missed the bustle and turmoil of Washington. Inactivity always made him restless.

He found Lucretia superintending two Negro women at the conical-shaped dairy house directly down the slope from the ice house. As the blocks of ice melted, the cold water ran directly underground to the damp, moist regions of the dairy. The ingenious idea was Lucretia's own.

She turned at the sound of his footsteps. Her pale cheeks were slightly flushed from her exertion. Henry thought of a wild rose as he looked at her.

"It is so good to be home," she said with a lilt in her voice.

For a moment he did not reply. A guilty pang shot through him. Not for the world would he have confessed to her that at times the daily routine of a country squire bored him. He longed for the stress and struggle of Washington. Sometimes at the capital he had wished for the peace and quiet of Ashland. That was life, he thought philosophically, always wanting what one did not have. Everyone did not have such singleness of purpose and desire as Lucretia with her love for the land and Ashland.

"Ashland is all anyone could wish for," he told her gently and not quite truthfully. For a moment he almost believed it as he heard the hum of bees in the honeysuckle and saw the two little girls playing with their dolls beside the hollyhock border.

Lucretia's eyes traveled upward to a second-story window where black Mammy Lottie was rocking back and forth with a palm-leaf fan in her hand.

"If only poor dear Theodore could be well again—"

Her husband followed the gaze of her eyes. Their eldest son had fallen from a horse and incurred a severe head injury. His recovery was slow and uncertain.

"He is getting all the care that medical science can provide," Henry reminded her.

She bit her lip in anxious concern. "It seems to me that we are having more than our share of troubles. Do you suppose that Tom will ever—mend his ways?"

Her husband rubbed his chin. Their second son, so full of life and action and *joie de vivre,* was giving them more than a little concern. Like many young Kentuckians of his day, he was said to be too fond of the bottle and the gaming table.

"Oh, I don't know," Clay said indulgently. "I wouldn't worry too much about him. I remember once when I was slightly older than he is now that I was very lively one night at a banquet. I leaped to the table and executed a *pas seul* all the way from the head to the foot. The other guests applauded loudly to the sound of shattered glass and china. Next morning I was presented with a bill for one hundred and twenty dollars—which I paid."

His wife gave a proper shudder. "That must have been before I married you."

"No, it wasn't," Henry Clay insisted. "My practice began to pick up about the time I married you. Before that I was as poor as the proverbial church mouse. I couldn't have raised that much then."

"I wonder what Mary Mentelle would say if Tom cut such a caper," Lucretia mused. "She is a charming girl. I think she is a good influence for our boy."

"I'm thankful she is French and not English," Clay observed, his eyes twinkling. "I'd rather have a French daughter-in-law than an English one any day. While you are having romantic notions, how do you like young Martin Duralde?"

"Very much," Lucretia replied. "I'm sure there's a wedding in the offing. I'm afraid he will be taking Susan all the way to New Orleans to live."

"Very likely," Clay agreed. "After all, his plantation is in Louisiana. It isn't as though she will be among strangers. Your sister Nancy and her husband are there, not to mention my brother John."

A great many changes occurred while Clay was home at Ashland. The following year the eldest Clay daughter married the handsome young planter and went south to live. In 1823 young James Erwin came up from Tennessee and, after a whirlwind courtship, carried off sixteen-year-old

Anne. That same year Lucretia, her mother's namesake, died. Time and change were lessening the family circle.

Clay had served in the Kentucky legislature in 1822. There was a singing triumph in his heart when they nominated him on November 18, 1822, for the presidency. Missouri had also promised her support, and a part of the Ohio assembly cautiously approved him. The highest office in the land was beckoning him on. It seemed to him that he had been moving toward this goal ever since his boyhood days with Chancellor Wythe.

With his usual optimistic nature Henry Clay could see only victory ahead. He forgot that he had powerful opponents. He ignored the most powerful opponent of all— Andrew Jackson of Tennessee.

In 1823 he returned to Congress after an absence of more than two years. As usual, he was elected Speaker.

With joy he championed President Monroe's words in his annual message to Congress. The President had warned: "The American continents, by the free and independent conditions which they have assumed and maintained, are henceforth not to be considered as subjects for future colonization by any European powers." At last the Chief Executive was advocating what he, Henry Clay, had been dreaming for years. Nearly three years ago he had been spokesman for the House of Representatives when he announced that they were ready to support the President whenever he recognized the South American governments.

Now in the message to Congress (which was to become known as the Monroe Doctrine) President Monroe had gone beyond recognition and warned European countries that the United States expected them to observe a strictly "hands off" policy.

The speech was plain speaking that warmed Clay's heart. It should deter Spain from trying to regain her lost colonies in South America, and it should discourage her allies England and Russia from aiding her. It should bring comfort to the neighbors to the south.

In 1824 Henry Clay hoped that America would recognize Greece in her struggle for independence. Wherever the banners of freedom were unfurled, Henry Clay's heart beat with sympathy. But the time was not yet ripe for that country's independence or recognition. Although the Greek Revolution had begun in 1821, the Turks continued to ravage the little country for years. Although European powers lent Greece some aid, Congress, wary of becoming embroiled in European politics, turned down Clay's resolution to recognize Greece.

There were more pressing matters close at home. The main question to be settled was the tariff. For Clay there was but one course: a protective tariff, internal improvements, a national bank to further and finance a growing America. These were the parts of the great whole known as the American system which dominated his thinking.

He found a keen antagonist in Congress this year in Daniel Webster from Massachusetts. Webster was no stranger to the Kentuckian, for he had represented New Hampshire in the House from 1813 to 1817. Now he had changed his residence and was back once more for another four-year term from another state.

Clay liked the stocky, broad-shouldered, dark-complexioned man with the beetling black eyebrows. He admired the other's mellifluous voice which flowed as smoothly as bourbon aged in wood.

"He would more than likely compare it with New England apple cider," Clay chuckled. "The man is a real orator. I'd rather have him with me than against me. Well, we may argue on the floor of the House, but I still enjoy a truce when I can hear him describe the joys of Marshfield, his farm up in New Hampshire, and the merits of Goliath, his prize ram. He loves his livestock as much as I love my race horses down in Kentucky. If only he could overcome his sectionalism and realize that this nation is made up of the Middle States, the West and the South as well as New England, he could render a real service to the country."

But Daniel Webster did not agree with Henry Clay that a high tariff would benefit the entire nation. New Englanders wanted a low tariff because they felt it would stimulate foreign trade. Southerners wanted a low tariff because they wished to trade their cotton for tax-free English manufactured goods. They were ranged against the West and the Middle States who were sure that growing business went hand in hand with internal improvements and the revenue from a high tariff with which to pay for them.

"Daniel Webster of Massachusetts and Robert Hayne of South Carolina! Sometimes politics makes strange bedfellows," Clay commented wryly to himself.

The Tariff Bill passed by a narrow margin. It was the calm before the storm, the truce before the battle. The real contest would come in the presidential race. Clay knew that well.

There would be no party lines in this race. The Federalist party had gradually faded after the victorious ending of the War of 1812. In the election of 1824, five men, all Democratic-Republicans, sought the office of president. They were John Quincy Adams, Secretary of State, from New England; William H. Crawford of Georgia; John C. Calhoun of South Carolina; Henry Clay of Kentucky; and Andrew Jackson of Tennessee.

With the coming of summer the presidential candidates had settled down in earnest to the business of the election. Before long, Calhoun dropped out of the race and was nominated without opposition for vice-president. Crawford had been incapacitated for months by illness, but still he did not withdraw his name.

Adams, Clay and Jackson were left in the race. His opponents did not fear fifty-five-year-old Jackson too much. Adams was New England's favorite son. Clay, who had been nominated in November, 1822, by the Kentucky legislature, lost no time in attempting to turn the West against Jackson. The presidential campaign increased in bitterness as the weeks went by. There were rumors and counter rumors. At last, election time arrived. When the final count was in, Jackson had ninety-nine electoral votes, Adams eighty-four, Crawford forty-one and Clay thirty-seven. Clay was out of the race. He had suffered his first serious defeat.

Being human, he was disappointed; but being Clay, he was undismayed. There was one consolation. Jackson did not have a majority and, according to the Constitution, a majority was necessary for election. The Constitution provided that the House of Representatives must now choose a candidate from the three highest candidates. Henry Clay smiled grimly. If he could not be president, he would be a president-maker.

When Clay returned to Washington in December, 1824, Lucretia remained at Ashland, pleading that they must consider expense. Had she known what lay ahead, she would probably have reconsidered and been at her husband's side. But distances were long and Lucretia could see no good reason to leave Ashland. There was no way for her to foresee the tangled web of circumstances that would engulf the Kentucky statesman before he returned home again.

Henry Clay found bachelor lodgings at a boarding house on Ninth Street in the capital. Another congressman from Kentucky and a former student of Clay's, Bob Letcher, was with him.

As leader of the West in the House, Clay was courted by the friends of all three candidates. In spite of the seriousness of the situation, it had its humorous aspects.

Alone in their rooms at night, Clay would walk back and forth, his hands thrust deep in his pockets, discussing his problems with Bob Letcher. He was glad he had a friend with whom to share them.

"Poor Crawford!" Clay exclaimed. "He is out of the picture. He has been an invalid since his paralytic stroke last year. They say he may not have long to live."

Letcher raised his eyebrows. "That leaves Jackson and Adams."

Clay replied in even tones, which had a cold dislike behind

them. "As I wrote to a friend not long ago, 'I cannot believe that killing twenty-five hundred English at New Orleans qualifies Jackson for the various, difficult and complicated duties of the chief magistrate.' "

Letcher looked thoughtfully at Clay's long, intelligent face. How much of the Speaker's feeling was jealousy? How much was good judgment? Folks were saying that Clay was already looking four years ahead to the next election. If the West furnished a president this time, certainly the voters would not choose another from the same section the next time.

"Look at how Jackson handled the Florida situation in 1818," Clay was saying. "Military show, bombast, cruelty and outright murder. No, I can't see Andrew Jackson in the president's chair."

"That leaves one man."

Clay's eyes were troubled. "Yes, I know. John Quincy Adams. I admit I never cared for him as an individual. He was a source of constant irritation to me at Ghent. We just don't speak the same language, but he is a better man than Jackson. In fact, he is the only possible choice. He is honest. I'd say that he is incorruptible. He believes in a protective tariff. He was Secretary of State when the South American republics were recognized and the Monroe Doctrine was issued. He is in favor of internal improvements. Why, come to think of it, he believes in the American system almost as much as I do."

"Then you intend to vote for him?" Letcher asked.

"I suppose I do," Clay replied. "However, I'm in no hurry. Let them guess a little longer."

He still had not declared his intentions when an anonymous letter appeared in a Philadelphia newspaper. It charged that Clay would vote for Adams for president. In return Adams would make Clay Secretary of State. It was signed "A Member of Congress from Pennsylvania."

As a matter of fact, Adams was Clay's only possible choice. Not only was Jackson his personal enemy, but he believed in no part of the American system. On the other hand, Clay was the best man available for Secretary of State. If Adams won the election and offered him the place, he would only be doing what many Americans thought was right. But this anonymous letter writer indicated a foul connivance between the two men.

When Clay read the accusation, he turned white-hot with anger. Although the election in the House was only a week away, he published a letter in the Washington *National Intelligencer*. It called on the writer of the anonymous letter to declare himself.

He was, Clay said, "a base and infamous calumniator, a dastard and a liar; and if he dare unveil himself and avow his name, I will hold him responsible, as I here admit myself to be, to all the laws which govern and regulate men of honor."

All the tongues in Washington wagged. Who was this anonymous letter writer? Did Mr. Clay's words mean a duel? What would happen now?

The answer to Clay's letter came a few days later like a clap of thunder. The author of the letter was the eccentric George Kremer of Pennsylvania, who had been sent to Congress from an isolated country district.

"I can't fight a battle with George Kremer," Clay protested to his friend Bob Letcher. "As the Scots would say, the man is 'daft.' He would probably arrive at the dueling grounds in that ridiculous leopardskin coat he wears summer and winter. The idea of meeting him is unthinkable."

"Kremer would never have thought of this idea by himself," Letcher said. "Andrew Jackson must be behind it."

Henry Clay drew himself up to his full height. "I shall demand a full investigation by Congress."

The investigation took place, but Kremer could produce no evidence to show a bargain between Clay and Adams. The Kentuckian's friends felt more than ever that it was a scheme of Andrew Jackson's. Now Clay was even more certain where he should throw his influence. He turned his votes to Adams, and the man from New England was elected.

President John Quincy Adams now offered the post of Secretary of State to Henry Clay. He accepted it. The Kremer incident had not served its purpose, if that purpose was to intimidate Clay. Neither had it intimidated Adams, who considered Clay the best-qualified man for the job. But Clay had gained an implacable enemy whose goal was the same as Clay's—the presidency. The enemy, of course, was Andrew Jackson.

Probably the four years from 1824 to 1828 were the unhappiest of Clay's life. In the first place, he was not suited to the confinement of four walls. He longed to release his pent-up energy in debate as he had once done on the floor of Congress. Instead, every day was a ceaseless round of toil and drudgery at his desk.

At least one good thing grew out of his association with President Adams, the man he had once called Old Surly. Clay grew to appreciate his chief's dedicated devotion to duty and his rock-bound fidelity to the Union.

The scene in politics had undergone a change. The Federalist party had expired with Monroe. On the national scene now were the National Republicans, followers of Adams, Clay and Webster. Later they would be called Whigs. Their opposition, followers of Jackson, Calhoun and Crawford, would become the Democratic party. The National Republicans believed in a powerful central government. The Democrats advocated strong state governments as opposed to control of the country by federal power.

Clay had a dream realized when, after much arguing and indecision, the United States voted to send two representatives to the Pan-American Congress at Panama in 1826. The Jackson men fought the measure all the way, but public opinion prevailed. True, one American died on the way, and the other arrived at his destination after the other representatives had gone home. Nevertheless, the United

States had shown her colors, and Henry Clay was overjoyed.

He had little at home to make him happy. Twelve-year-old Eliza had died in 1825 when the family was en route to Washington. Susan Clay Duralde had succumbed to yellow fever the same year in New Orleans. Theodore had never recovered from his head injury. Tom was working in Philadelphia. Henry, Jr., was studying hard at West Point. Only James and John remained with their parents.

Weary from a tiresome day in the State Department and harassed by the unceasing attacks of the opposition, Clay was not helped by returning at the end of the day to a weeping wife and two unhappy little boys.

"These are all we have left of our eleven children," Lucretia sobbed one afternoon. "The living ones are scattered. Henrietta, Lucretia, Eliza and Laura lie in their graves. Only these two are with us."

He looked at her helplessly. There was little left in this broken, faded, prematurely old woman to remind him of the gay, vivacious girl he had married. Heaven knows, he thought sadly, she has had enough to age her.

"Go and lie down," he told her gently. "I will take care of the boys until suppertime."

After she had gone upstairs, James and John began to climb all over their father in the big armchair. They knew a search through his pockets would disclose a packet of gaily striped peppermint lozenges, a confection of which they and he were very fond.

Before long they had settled down contentedly in his lap. Clay had a long arm around each little son. There was a tell-tale bulge in the cheeks of all three.

"When I was a boy in Virginia—" he began, stretching out his legs luxuriously toward the hearth flames.

Although Lucretia Clay did not care greatly for public life, she did her dutiful best to make their home in Washington a social center. Many people in the capital and elsewhere hoped he would be the next president. In 1827 the

Clays rented the Stephen Decatur house and opened wide its doors.

Since 1823 James Brown had been minister to France. Nancy Hart Brown sent home to her sister from time to time French china, fine paintings and other foreign articles that lent an air of distinction to the Clay residence. A gay crowd moved constantly in and out of the house while its master and mistress, hiding their disappointment over the last election and their grief over their private affairs, presented a brave front to the world.

But the National Republicans, especially Henry Clay, were living on borrowed time. There would be another election year in 1828, when John Quincy Adams would run for re-election. Andrew Jackson was waiting, waiting, waiting.

At length election activities went into full swing. The old cry of "bargain and intrigue" rose up above the tumult. The loudest voice was that of old John Randolph—Randolph of Roanoke—who, according to his enemies, was mad as a March hare. Perhaps he was—mad with hate at Henry Clay. He had called Clay the "Judas of the West" when Clay accepted the post of Secretary of State under Adams.

Now the attack had begun again. "Let Judas have his thirty pieces of silver!" he cried shrilly. They could "go to buy a potter's field in which to inter this miserable Constitution of ours."

Then he meandered on, stating that there was an alliance "between Old Massachusetts and Kentucky—between the frost of January and young blithe, buxom and blooming May—the eldest daughter of Virginia—young Kentucky—not so young, however, as not to make a prudent match, and sell her charms for their full value."

It was a filthy speech, but he could not be quieted.

"I was defeated, horse, foot and dragoons—cut up—and clean broke down—by the coalition of Blifil and Black George—by the combination, unheard of till then, of the Puritan with the blackleg."

All Washington was aghast. A blackleg was nothing more than a crooked gambler. Randolph had reference to Clay's fondness for cards. This time the Virginian had gone too far.

Henry Clay lost no time in sending him a challenge:

Sir:

Your unprovoked attack on my character, in the Senate of the United States, on yesterday, allows me no other alternative than that of demanding personal satisfaction. The necessity of any preliminary discussion or explanations being suspended by the notoriety and the indisputable existence of the injury to which I refer, my friend General Jesup, who will present you this note, is fully authorized by me forthwith to agree to the arrangements suited to the interview proposed.

Your obedient servant,

H. CLAY

The duel took place a few days later across the Potomac River from Georgetown. Not wishing to alarm Lucretia, her husband had kept the matter a secret from her. Her cousin, Tom Benton—Senator Thomas Hart Benton of Missouri— had almost given the whole thing away the previous evening when he called at the Clay home.

Henry had been surprised to see their visitor. The political differences between the two men since Jackson's defeat in 1824 had kept them separate.

Tom Benton served under Old Hickory in the War of 1812—and he has the same blind hero worship for him that too large a part of the country seems to be indulging in, Clay thought as the big, florid-faced man was ushered into their back parlor.

As usual Clay was the perfect host. He rose to his feet and held out his hand. "Why, Tom! This is a surprise."

Senator Benton seemed a trifle embarrassed, but Clay's frank and cordial manner soon put an end to that. In a short time Lucretia's cousin was chatting away about family affairs and exchanging political opinions—very carefully—with her husband.

Not until Clay had carried two sleepy little boys off to bed and their mother had retired for the night did the master of the house learn the purpose of Benton's visit.

The Senator gave a nod toward the upper floor. "She knows nothing about tomorrow?"

Henry shook his head. "Not a word. She has enough to bear without my increasing the load. If I escape unscathed, there will be time enough to tell her. If not—"

His face was a picture of gloom. Tom Benton cleared his throat. He seemed at a loss as to how to proceed.

"Yes?" Clay asked. "What is it?"

The other's florid face turned a deeper hue. "I hardly know how to say it—and I'm seldom at a loss for words. Blood is considerably thicker than water, you know. In spite of our political differences—damme, Henry! You have my best wishes for tomorrow."

Henry seized the hand of his wife's cousin in a grip of steel. The Kentuckian's features were trembling with emotion.

"God bless you, Tom!" he returned huskily. "Whatever happens, I'm glad you came tonight."

As Clay's carriage rolled toward the dueling grounds, he thought of last night's scene. He had been singularly touched by the Senator's visit. The carriage rolled on and stopped. Clay climbed down. He was followed by his seconds, General Jesup and Senator Johnson.

Randolph's carriage was already there. So were his seconds, Colonel Tatnall and General Hamilton. And Randolph himself—Clay gave a startled gasp. The tall spare form of his opponent was wrapped in a long white dressing gown.

"He's as mad as Kremer!" the Kentuckian muttered under his breath. Then his face hardened. "Mad or not, he shall answer to me for his insults."

The seconds went through the customary procedures. A coin was tossed to determine who would have the best position. Randolph's second won. He placed the tall, emaciated

Virginian with his back to the setting sun and counted off ten paces. On the indicated spot Henry Clay took his stand.

Just before the signal was given, John Randolph's pistol went off.

"It was an accident!" Henry Clay called courteously.

Again the two men took their places. This time each duelist fired. Randolph's bullet hit a stump behind Clay. Clay's shot kicked up the gravel behind Randolph.

The Kentuckian was disgusted. "This is child's play!" he muttered.

He took aim more carefully next time. Randolph fired into the air.

"I do not fire at you, Mr. Clay!" he called in his high treble voice.

For a moment Clay thought his bullet had struck home. Then his antagonist advanced to meet him.

"You owe me a coat!" he exclaimed, throwing back his dressing gown and disclosing a bullet hole in his garment.

Clay had broken out in a cold sweat. There was a feeling of thankfulness in his heart that the other had not been injured.

"I am glad the debt is no greater," he exclaimed fervently.

The duel was over. According to the standards of the time, honor had been satisfied. Presently the two carriages with their occupants drove off the field. The affair had ended.

To be sure, the Jackson adherents painted a black picture of Clay, who had asked for the duel in the first place. Even President Adams scolded him, but Clay did not mind greatly. He had become accustomed by now to the worst that people could say about him. All he regretted was the bad example he might have set to others. With his usual sense of humor he stated:

"I must, however, say that my present feelings are in a state of composure and satisfaction which I should not have enjoyed if the occasion had not occurred. We are strange beings."

The "bargain and corruption" charges went on. Clay continued to deny them. The presidential campaign was bitter on each side. For a time Clay was certain that Adams would be re-elected. Then little by little he saw the tide turning. Toward the end of 1828 he wrote to young Henry at West Point:

"General Jackson, without doubt, will be elected. . . . I consider the matter as decided."

There was no mistaking the manner in which it was decided. General Jackson received a majority of ninety-five electoral votes.

Clay was filled with disgust at the rejoicing, shouting, trampling mob that broke glass and smashed china at the White House on Inauguration Day. If this was Andrew Jackson's greatly vaunted Democracy—

The year 1828 had been a long and sad one. Neither he nor his wife was in good health. Nancy Hart Brown was slowly dying of cancer in Paris. The doctors had pronounced Theodore hopelessly insane. And Tom had not yet found himself. He had even served a short jail sentence in Philadelphia for disturbing the peace. Henry was glad that his stay in Washington was nearing its end. Yet his usual optimism prevailed for a time. At a farewell dinner he proposed the toast: "Let us never despair of the Republic!"

Soon the Clays sold their furniture, turned over the keys of the Decatur house to its new occupants, and took passage for Kentucky.

For the second time since he had entered politics Henry Clay was leaving public life. But not for long. No doubt the Jackson administration would be a sorry mess—and there would always be another presidential election. This was only the opening round of the fight!

15

HOME AND BACK AGAIN

THE SPRING OF 1829 FOUND THE CLAYS AT ASHLAND ONCE more. The roads in Kentucky were deplorable. It had taken Henry Clay sixteen days to bring his family by coach over the sixty-four miles from Maysville on the Ohio River.

For a time Ashland wove its charm about the long-absent master. He mended his fences and planted his crops. He acquired fifty pure-blooded Merino sheep from western Pennsylvania. Livestock always interested him more than husbandry. He bought another hundred acres of land adjoining Ashland and rejoiced at the increase to his estate. Washington with its schemes and intrigues seemed part of another world.

But the period was not completely halcyon. Before the end of 1829, Clay's mother, stepfather and brother John had died in close succession. A little later the news came that Nancy Hart Brown had died in Paris. By now Theodore was in an institution. Overcome by sorrow, Lucretia retired within herself and seldom left the house. Clay would have returned to politics anyway, but the grief-stricken atmosphere of Ashland may have hastened the move.

From the first day of his return to Kentucky, Henry Clay did not hesitate to voice his disapproval of the military hero in the White House. The first blast came at a public dinner in Clay's honor. It was a barbecue at Fowler's Gardens on the outskirts of Lexington. Three thousand people from all over Kentucky had gathered there to eat, drink and listen to the renowned orator.

Clay spoke against the spoils system—the practice of sweeping out old political officeholders and installing new ones. Its name came from the old proverb—"To the victors belong the spoils." The custom had not been unknown in other administrations, but Old Hickory was the first to make a general sweep of men from public office with no regard for the fitness of newcomers to fill the jobs.

"If a man wanted to be a dictator, he would go about it in just this way," Clay said. "If an ambitious president sought the overthrow of our government, he would begin by proclaiming by his official acts that the greatest public virtue was ardent devotion to him. He would say, as monarchs have said, 'I am the state.' He would dismiss all from public employment who did not belong to the true faith. He would stamp upon the whole official corps of government one homogeneous character, and infuse into it one uniform principle of action."

In 1830 Jackson vetoed a bill to provide for construction of a road between Maysville and Lexington. The act gave him a two-pronged satisfaction. The veto struck at a vital part of the American system and affected also Clay, who traveled the Maysville Road on his way to Washington.

In 1831 his son-in-law James Erwin bought the General Trotter farm adjoining Ashland. Here, he declared, he would bring his family a part of every year. The Clays were overjoyed to have their only remaining daughter so near. That same year Clay purchased the neighboring estate of Mansfield for his son Tom, who had left behind his youthful indiscretions, settled down and married Mary Mentelle. Henry, Jr., graduated second in his class at West Point. In spite of depletion by death and tragedy, the family seemed to be approaching better days.

Meanwhile more and more pressure was being put on him to return to Washington. It was pressure to which he readily responded. All his life—since the days with Chancellor Wythe —there had existed in his heart the hope, the wish, the fervent belief that someday he would occupy the presidential chair. Unconsciously each move of his political life was directed toward that goal.

Since his return from the capital in 1829 he had traveled extensively throughout the South, where he was warmly received. He became keenly aware that the Tariff of 1828, which Congress had passed during the last year of Adams' administration, was a foremost issue before the people.

Like the Tariff of 1824 it increased the duties on goods brought from abroad. When it had become a law, the manufacturing North was pleased. Without competition from English markets, they could demand and get reasonable prices for their goods. The cotton-growing South was aghast. Always they had sold much of their crop in England and traded the proceeds for duty-free goods there. Clearly the sale of cotton would suffer if English trade fell off because of a high tariff. And what was more, the southerners must now buy their manufactured goods at a high price from the North. The South grew increasingly bitter. Soon they were referring to the Tariff of 1828 as the "Tariff of Abominations."

Removed from the scene of action to Kentucky, Henry Clay watched to see what would happen. The next development was the Doctrine of Nullification. Presented to its citizens by the South Carolina legislature, this doctrine claimed that the states had drawn up the national Constitution and set up the central government. To this government they had given certain powers. If the federal government went beyond its powers and passed a law not provided for in the Constitution, any state could refuse to obey such a law.

Down in Kentucky, Henry Clay sizzled like a firecracker at utterances that he regarded as subversive. Each mail brought fresh news of the increasing storm. South Carolina, especially, was in a ferment. All over the South the cotton planters were sympathizing with their sister state. Meanwhile the North stood firm. The Tariff of 1828 was a law. The South would have to obey it.

At Ashland, Mammy Chloe sent her most tempting delicacies to the dining room and watched her master's plate return almost untouched. Clay's saddle mare in her stall waited in vain for the lump of sugar that she had learned to expect from her owner. Aaron Dupuy, the Negro who had grown old and been replaced by his son Charles in the Clay family's service, heard sharp words from Henry Clay for the first time in his life. James and John Clay disappeared quickly whenever they heard their father's footsteps. Lucretia sighed and waited. She had seen her husband upset over public affairs before but never so badly as he was now.

Through the kitchen window one winter day Mammy Chloe watched his tall spare form tramping through the newly fallen snow in the semicircle known as Clay's Walk. He had trampled a path with his high boots. The action did not go unnoted in the kitchen.

Presently sixteen-year-old James Clay entered the morning room. He was grinning broadly as he sat down on the arm of his mother's chair.

"You seem amused," she observed. "What is it?"

James chuckled. "I overheard Sally in the kitchen talking to Mammy Chloe. She said, apropos of Father's spirited gallop around the back woodland, that he was so angry he was melting the snow right under his feet."

Lucretia smiled. "And what did Mammy reply to that?"

"Oh, she reproved poor Sally severely. She said Father had a great deal on his mind. She added that he was well aware that the country was going to rack and ruin without him in Washington to look after things. She made the sage comment that he had been away from the capital long enough and would be going back any time now."

Lucretia sighed. "She is probably right. Your father always gets restless when he is away from Washington for long. And people want him to be there. He is a great man, James."

"That he is," the boy agreed readily. His face was serious now. "He will be president yet—I hope."

In a little while Henry Clay returned to the house. He stopped in the back hall only long enough to exchange his boots for house slippers. His face was ruddy from cold and exercise as he entered the morning room.

"Didn't I hear carriage wheels?" he asked eagerly. "Surely the papers will bring news of the Webster-Hayne debate in Congress. How I should have liked to be there!"

Sixteen-year-old James grinned at his mother. "It would have been a three-way affair," he remarked *sotto voce* to her. "I can't imagine Father's being in Congress without making a speech."

The corners of Lucretia Clay's mouth twitched, but she shook her head at James. Although she could not approve such levity on his part toward his father, the boy was right. Speechmaking came as naturally as breathing to Harry of the West.

Meanwhile he was searching through the day's mail on the table. "Ah, here it is," he said, his eyes lighting up. He spread out the Washington newspaper. "Let me see. The usual states' rights protests from Senator Hayne—Constitution framed by the states—central government has no right to establish a protective tariff that will benefit one section of the country at the expense of another— Bosh! Can't they see that what benefits one part of the country will eventually benefit the whole?"

He shook the sections of the paper into place. "Now! Let's see what Mr. Webster said in reply." For a few moments he read intently. Then his wide mouth broke into a smile. "Listen to this, James and Lucretia. First, he refuted every argument Robert Hayne presented, point by point. Daniel Webster is a master of logic. There is no doubt about it. But he is much more. He is a statesman of the first rank."

He held the paper at arm's length before him and began to read aloud: " 'As for the Doctrine of Nullification, talk about it as you will, it goes the length of revolution. When my eyes shall be turned to behold for the last time the sun in heaven, may I not see him shining on the broken fragments of a once glorious Union; on States dissevered, discordant, belligerent; on a land rent with civil feuds, or drenched, it may be, in fraternal blood. Let their last feeble and lingering glance rather behold the glorious flag of a republic now known and honored throughout the earth; not a stripe missing, not a single star obscured, bearing for its motto that sentiment dear to every true American heart—Liberty and Union, now and forever, one and inseparable!' "

Clay laid the paper down and surveyed his audience. Lucretia's eyes were suspiciously moist. James's youthful face still held the glow awakened by the inspired phrases he had just heard. Henry Clay was more at peace with himself than he had been for months.

His blue eyes held their old familiar twinkle as he leaned forward to stir the fire. "I couldn't have said it better myself," he announced.

The people of the nation watched day by day to learn the outcome of South Carolina's stand. After all, the President of the United States was a southerner and a cotton grower. What would he say? They had their answer in April, 1830.

The Democrats, as Andrew Jackson's party was called now, held a banquet in Washington, D.C., on Jefferson's birthday. President Jackson was asked to give the toast. Here was the crucial moment. Was he for or against Nullification? The old veteran of the Battle of New Orleans rose and stood with a martial air.

"Our Union! It must be preserved!" he announced in ringing tones.

Down in Kentucky, Henry Clay received the news with mixed emotions. He despised Andrew Jackson, yet he must give him an unwilling admiration for his stand on Nullification. Clay knew the southern mind well enough to recognize that belief in a low tariff was an inseparable part of every southerner. Yet a southerner in the president's chair had realized that the Union, not the tariff, was paramount.

Clay stirred uneasily at his desk chair in the small octagonal-shaped library at Ashland. With him, too, belief in the Union was an inescapable ideal—but did gruff, uncouth, unlettered old Andrew Jackson, idol of the common people though he was, have the diplomacy, tact, sensitiveness—frankly, the brains—to deal with the fiery, impetuous, quick-on-the-trigger South Carolinians? Clay thought not.

When Clay was elected to Congress by the Kentucky legislature in 1831, he went gladly. This time he was a member of the Senate. He smiled ruefully as he reminded himself that he was with the old men now. Oh, well, what did it matter? The point was that he was needed, and he was back and would work. How he would work!

Soon after Congress opened, Clay made a speech, "In Defense of the American System." He pointed out that the American system had produced a sound currency and an overflowing treasury. Duties on European products that competed with American manufactures must never be reduced. Never until foreign nations would admit American products duty-free!

"Free trade!" he concluded. "The call for free trade is as unavailing as the cry of a spoiled child in its nurse's arms for the moon or the stars that glitter in the firmament of heaven. It never has existed; it never will exist!"

He won his hearers as he always won them. The Tariff of Abominations was repealed. A new tariff replaced it which Congress hoped would be more acceptable to the South. There were lower duties on some foreign goods, but duties on competitive goods were retained. This was the Tariff of 1832.

The major issue of 1832 was the recharter of the Second Bank of the United States. (The First Bank of the United States had expired in 1811.) Chartered in 1816, the Second Bank had seen the country through the financial chaos that followed the War of 1812. It had brought about a sound currency system for the United States and by this time was a strong part of the national life.

Its charter would not expire until 1836. However, the keen politician in Clay—he had long since ceased trying to separate the statesman and the politician—noted that here was a campaign issue worth considering. He was in the thick of the political campaign at Baltimore when he decided to carry the fight into the enemy's territory.

"If you petition for a renewal of the bank's charter at once, Jackson must sign the bill or veto it," Clay craftily told Nicholas Biddle, the bank's president. "After his openly expressed hostility to the bank, he can hardly renew its charter. If he vetoes it, he will lose the vote of the West and probably Pennsylvania. We have him on the horns of a dilemma!"

After careful consideration Biddle applied for a recharter. Clay smiled, thinking that Jackson's refusal to sign the bank bill would spell his political doom. But he smiled too soon. Old Hickory vetoed the bill and accompanied the veto with a message picturing the bank as a monster sucking the lifeblood of the people.

It was a battle to the death between Jackson and the bank. Clay was certain that the bank—and he—would win.

But he underestimated the power of the common people —the force of Jackson's exalted Democracy—that had put the old General in the White House. The rank and file of Americans paid little attention to the cartoons in the newspapers that favored Clay. One depicted Jackson as a burglar wielding a battering-ram at the bank's entrance. Another showed him as a Don Quixote shattering his lance against the bank. Still another showed "King Andrew" accepting a scepter from the devil. However, the masses of the people saw Andrew Jackson as a St. George killing the dragon—their mortal enemy, the bank.

When the election was over, Clay had received 49 electoral votes and Jackson 219. Henry Clay had lost the presidency for the second time. What he could not understand was that the humblest Americans in an overwhelming Democratic surge had accepted old Andrew Jackson as their champion.

16

THE COMPROMISE OF 1833

"It cannot be! Great God, it cannot be!"

Henry Clay still clutched the newspaper as he sprang to his feet. His young son James thrust his head in a door of the octagonal study at Ashland.

"You sound upset, Father. What is wrong?"

Without a word Clay pointed to the offending newspaper. James picked it up and scanned it hastily. His boyish eyes were troubled as he turned back to his father.

"This could mean civil war."

"It could and will unless something is done quickly," Clay returned. His face was grim. "South Carolina has talked nullification, but now she is actually putting it into effect. This Ordinance of Nullification declares the Tariff of 1832 null and void and forbids the collection of duties after February 1, 1833. That is only two months away. As though that were not bad enough, President Jackson threatens to adopt force to bring the South Carolinians to their senses. If he does that, he will plunge the country into chaos and confusion."

"Yet he is trying to enforce the tariff," James ventured. "And you are for the tariff."

"With all my heart," Clay agreed. "That is one matter on which Andrew Jackson and I agree. But I do not believe in this Doctrine of Nullification. The Union *must* be preserved!"

"That's what General Jackson said," James exclaimed.

"Remember? 'The Federal Union! It must and shall be preserved.' "

Henry Clay drew himself to his full height. His hand trembled slightly as he swept a pile of letters and papers into the desk drawer.

"There is an old saying, my son, that politics makes strange bedfellows. Though I cannot under any circumstances imagine myself occupying the bed of Andrew Jackson, the enemies of the Union are my enemies. If by chance a scoundrel happens to be on the right side of the question, I shall still fight my enemies even though I fight alongside the scoundrel. He shall account to me at a later date."

It was now December, 1832. In a few days Clay returned to the Senate. James, who was on his way to work in Philadelphia, traveled with his father as far as Washington. The two heard nothing but talk of secession and nullification. Clay found Washington more like an armed camp than a national capital. By this time fiery old Andrew Jackson had issued a proclamation to the people of South Carolina. "Disunion by armed force is *treason*. Are you ready to incur its guilt?" he thundered.

South Carolina was rapidly burning her bridges. The militia was drilling. The people had elected a new governor. John Calhoun from his seat in the Senate was watching every opportunity to serve his native state.

After Clay reached Washington, Jackson asked Congress for the power to enforce law in South Carolina by military arms. This act, soon called by South Carolinians the "Bloody Bill," was known in Congress as the "Force Bill." Its passage was bitterly debated. Daniel Webster was on the President's side. The southern congressmen were with South Carolina. The conflagration seemed ready to burst into flames.

General opinion seemed to be that drastic measures were necessary to avert a catastrophe. Somehow the North and the South must be kept from going to war. Someone must lead them away from the dangerous brink. But who? John Randolph—Randolph of Roanoke—supplied the answer: "There is one man, and one man only, who can save this Union—that man is Henry Clay."

No one was more surprised at the old Virginian's words than Henry Clay himself. He had not dreamed that his ancient enemy would ever utter them. Yet in his heart he knew they were true. While he had always spoken with the courage of his convictions and had been listened to, he knew full well that he would be listened to if he merely spoke.

It went deeply against the grain to consider such a course. He despised Andrew Jackson with all the passion of his being. He would not and could not speak up for the Force Bill. He knew that the stubborn, strong-willed old man in the White House would never reverse his stand. Nor would Clay want him to, for he could not condone South Carolina's action. Yet no state could be allowed to disregard the laws of the land. The application of the Force Bill could lead only to open warfare. One avenue alone remained. That was the reduction of the tariff.

Henry Clay groaned. He had seen his efforts for internal improvements swept away. He had watched the bank destroyed. The tariff alone remained. If that went the way of the other measures, its passing would mark the end of the American system. It might mark the end of Henry Clay, politically speaking, if its erasure incurred sufficiently the wrath of the northern manufacturers. What was a man to do?

Sometime during the lonely watches of the night or the decisive hours of the day he made his resolution, announcing it in mid-February, 1833. It was the act of a brave man.

The issue was, he said, to avert civil war. "If there be any who want civil war, who want to see the blood of any portion of our countrymen split, I am not one of them. I wish to see war of no kind; but above all, I do not desire to see a civil war. When war begins, whether civil or foreign, no human sight is competent to foresee when, or how, or where it is to terminate. But when a civil war shall be lighted upon the bosom of our own happy land, and armies are marching, and commanders are winning the victories, and fleets are in motion on our coast, tell me, if you can, if any human being can tell its duration. God alone knows where such a war would end. In what state will our institutions be left? In what state our liberties? I want no war; above all, no war at home."

To avoid this war Henry Clay reversed his stand and offered up on the altar of his country's welfare the dream of a lifetime. He advocated the reduction of the tariff.

The bill passed the House "like a hurricane." With Webster opposing it, it lingered longer in the Senate. But at last it went through the upper house and was signed by Jackson. The Force Bill also passed the House and the Senate. Ten days later South Carolina nullified it, but it had become a dead issue, for the people of the state had accepted the new tariff bill—the Compromise of 1833.

That winter, as Clay was speaking in the Senate against secession and nullification, he heard a trembling, shrill, familiar voice. It was that of old John Randolph. Shaken and feeble, he had insisted upon being brought to the Senate.

"Raise me up!" he quavered. "I want to hear that voice again."

When Clay had finished his speech, he went in search of his onetime enemy. The wasted man was lying on a long couch in the hallway. Pity flooded the Kentuckian's heart as he looked at the old Virginian, knowing he was a dying man. What passed between them is not recorded, but in spite of their differences the two parted on friendly terms. The tradition persists, however, that John Randolph insisted upon being buried with his face to the West so that he might keep an eye on Henry Clay.

The affairs of 1833 brought drastic changes in the political field. Calhoun and much of the South now lined up with Clay, who was responsible for the reduction of the tariff. Webster and the other northerners, sickened by Jackson's attack on the United States Bank, turned to the Great Compromiser as the lesser of two evils.

Hating the bank with all his heart, the President had ill-advisedly drawn the government funds from the bank and deposited them in state banks of his own choosing. In the ensuing battle between Jackson and Biddle, a financial panic followed.

In addition to the bank fiasco, the North was concerned with Jackson's stand on the public lands. By the year 1832 the United States owned more than a billion acres of undeveloped land. This had been acquired by the Louisiana Purchase and the Northwest Territory. The people in the new states in the South and the West, where these lands lay, felt that they should have them free or be able to purchase them very cheaply. Henry Clay and his followers in the East and North did not agree. They thought the public lands belonged to everyone. Clay said these lands should be sold and the funds be divided among all the states for the purpose of building schools and carrying on internal improvements.

When Henry Clay proposed a bill to dispose of the public lands, Jackson did not veto it after it had passed both Houses. He merely killed it by keeping it in his possession until Congress adjourned. Thus Jackson became the father of the pocket veto.

Clay's voice rang out in protest. "We are in the midst of a revolution, hitherto bloodless, but rapidly tending toward a total change of the pure republican character of the government and to the concentration of all power in the hands of one man."

Clay felt so strongly on the subject of what he considered Jackson's unbridled powers that he led the Senate in an attempt to make a formal censure of the President. The condemnation was based on Jackson's removal of the national deposits from the Bank of the United States. Webster and Calhoun stood firm with Clay on that question during the rest of the Jackson administration. The three were known to their enemies as the Great Triumvirate. In spite of their efforts Jackson was adamant. They could go no further than the Senate in a public condemnation of the President. The House, where Henry Clay had once held control, stayed loyal to Jackson.

Each year the House attempted to force the Senate to expunge its offending motion of censure. Finally in 1837 a Democratic majority in the upper house forced the Secretary of the Senate to draw black lines across the words of the resolution in the *Journal* and write above them, "Expunged by order of the Senate, this —— day of ——, in the year of our Lord, 1837." The blanks were to be filled in by the Senate the following year. Henry Clay had received a major defeat in more than the presidential election.

Meanwhile in 1835 Henry Clay had written: "I am truly sick of Congress." Perhaps for a time he was sick of living. James Brown had died in Philadelphia that year. But that blow was light compared with the loss of his one remaining daughter. Anne Erwin had died at Lexington while her father was still in Washington.

He wrote to a friend: "She was so interwoven with every plan and prospect of passing the remnant of my days, that I feel that I have sustained a loss which can never be repaired. Henceforward, there is nothing before me in this world but duties."

But there had been so many duties. The victories were few. However, in 1835 Clay's efforts averted a war with France. Fiery old President Jackson was charging up and down and swearing that France must pay for damages incurred by American shipping during the Napoleonic Wars.

In unmistakable tones he announced that the debt would be paid at once, or French property would be seized in lieu of it.

Henry Clay shuddered. Jackson's saber rattling was a quick road to war. As chairman of the Senate Committee on Foreign Affairs, he immediately set in motion the wheels of diplomacy.

As long as I can keep the two nations talking, he reflected, they can't start fighting.

The situation cooled down. Great Britain entered the stage in 1836 as mediator. The same year the French government began making payments on the debt. War had been averted. Quietly and skillfully Henry Clay had guided the ship of state through stormy waters, although his hand was not openly the one at the helm.

In the election of 1836 Clay had not even secured the nomination. That dubious honor had been given by the Whigs (the successors of the old National Republicans) to General William Harrison, who was in turn badly defeated by Democratic Martin Van Buren, who had been vice-president since 1832. Jackson had trained him well to carry out his policies.

In late 1837 Clay returned wearily to Washington for a six-year term in the Senate. Yet there was a silver lining in the extremely dark cloud. As the days and weeks passed, Henry Clay's spirits lifted as he had not dreamed they would lift. The national financial depression did not lower them. Van Buren and his party were steadily losing ground. The Whigs were bound to win in 1840!

Before many months Washington drawing rooms were aflutter with the report that Henry Clay had gone around to the White House "to examine the premises, and to satisfy himself whether they would be likely to be in a tenantable condition about three years hence."

Harry of the West did not give up easily!

17

ONE FIGHT MORE

In 1839 Henry Clay, aged sixty-two, was ready and willing to receive the presidential nomination from the Whigs. They were prepared to snatch the scepter from "King Andrew's" party. Clay was the acknowledged leader of the Whigs. He had sought the office of president three times now and been disappointed for one reason or another on each occasion.

In the early fall of 1839 he carried the fight into the enemy's country. New York State he must have and New York State, he had heard, was not solidly for him.

With his son James he traveled to Buffalo, through central New York, up to Montreal and Quebec and down to fashionable Saratoga Springs. The springs were delightful in August. There he received the plaudits of the crowd in a manner befitting Prince Hal of Kentucky. He welcomed graciously Thurlow Weed, the "Dictator" of the Whig party in New York State, when that gentleman came to call on him in his suite. He had dealt with Mr. Weed before, and the results had not been too gratifying.

Mr. Weed knew beyond the shadow of a doubt that his state would not support Mr. Clay, but somehow he lacked the courage to say so. In all fairness to him, he tried to warn the Kentuckian.

"Mr. Clay, your stand on Abolition has offended the adherents of that group in New York," he informed the older man.

"Mr. Weed, I am in the habit of voicing my convictions," his listener replied. "The Abolitionists are pursuing a fatal course. They are stirring up the people of the free states against the people of the slave states. If they continue in their madness, they will plunge the country into civil war. Now Emancipation—"

"We cannot ignore the Abolitionist vote," Thurlow Weed insisted doggedly.

Clay raised his eyebrows. "What leads you to think I wish to? There are many middle-of-the-road men among them. They will support me."

Weed looked speculatively at Clay. "Mr. Webster conveniently removed himself from the scene when he went as ambassador to England."

There was a trace of hauteur in Clay's response. "I am not at all certain that Mr. Webster's presence would have helped me. I have heard rumors that he does not support me. It would not be the first time he was on the wrong side of a question."

The conference between Henry Clay and Thurlow Weed accomplished nothing. Clay regarded the latter's remarks as being of small consequence. It was unfortunate, perhaps, that he could not see their far-reaching results.

At the height of the presidential campaign Clay made the famous utterance that may have lost him the presidency. Urged to keep silent on the Abolition question, he replied: "I would rather be right than be president."

When the Whig convention met at Harrisburg in the latter part of 1839, the delegates again nominated William Harrison, the old hero of the Battle of Tippecanoe, which had taken place before the War of 1812.

Clay was angry and deeply hurt at not receiving the nomination. His immediate reaction was to give way to the temper he usually kept leashed. "My friends are not worth the powder and shot it would take to kill them!" he exclaimed.

When the heat of his passion had abated, he acted with

the generosity typical of his nature. After all, his party was his party, and his loyalty lay with them. Throughout the campaign he worked with all his might for the Whigs. Old General Harrison was elected by a large majority of the electors. John Tyler of Virginia became the vice-president. But an ominous note was sounded by the rise of the Liberty party (Abolitionists), whose candidate carried seven thousand of the popular vote.

Henry Clay continued his support of the Whig party. In every way he supported the new president, who died after a month in office.

At first Clay supported his successor, John Tyler; but the latter, to the disgust of many members of the Whig party, began to display Jacksonian tendencies, especially by involving themselves in a fight against the Bank of the United States. There was a split among the Whigs, and the majority of them turned toward Henry Clay.

All eyes were on them. Clay Clubs sprang up everywhere. "Justice to Harry of the West!" became their motto. It seemed as though the tide of fortune had turned at last in Clay's favor. Perhaps the long-sought victory would come in 1844 when the nation would choose a new president.

When Clay resigned from the Senate in 1842 with a somewhat flowery speech of farewell, the aging Jackson in the Hermitage down in Tennessee exclaimed with gleeful malice: "The old coon is really and substantially dead, skinned and buried—Clay's political career is closed forever."

But the General exulted too soon. Clay's prospects for the presidency in 1844 were very bright indeed—and growing brighter every day.

His friends continued to be more than a little uneasy. They knew their man. He could be suave, polished, urbane and courteous—and usually was. But when a conviction welled up in his heart, he lost no time in giving it voice.

Congressman Letcher wrote to a mutual friend:

The Old Prince must hereafter remain a little quiet and *hold his jaw*. In fact he must be *caged*—that's the point—*cage him*. But he swears by all the gods, he will keep cool and stay at home. I rather think he will be entirely prudent, tho' I have some occasional fears that he may write too many letters.

Congressman Letcher knew his friend. The fall of 1842 found Clay on a political tour of Ohio and Indiana. At Richmond, Indiana, a Quaker Abolitionist came forward and urged him to free his slaves.

The Kentuckian quietly reminded the speaker of his hatred for slavery and his belief in gradual emancipation as a cure for the evil. Then he turned and reminded the audience of what he had said a great many times before: the immediate freeing of the slaves would produce a fearful struggle between blacks and whites. As to his own slaves, some of them would not accept freedom if it were offered. Others were old, infirm and helpless. What would be their fate if they were turned loose?

With ill-advised irritation, Henry Clay turned to the Abolitionist and exclaimed: "Go home and mind your own business, and leave other people to take care of theirs. Limit your benevolent exertions to your own neighborhood—and you will be a better and wiser man than you have shown yourself."

The years were slipping by. Henry Clay was sixty-five now. He could not handle the barbs and shafts of his opponents with the ease that had once characterized him.

In the winter of 1842-43 Clay went to New Orleans to visit his son-in-law and grandchildren. Ostensibly it was a pleasure trip, but Henry Clay being Henry Clay, there was campaigning, too. The journey was a very happy occasion with the cheers of the crowds ringing in his ears to the tune of a popular song:

> Get out of the way, you're all unlucky,
> Clear the track for old Kentucky.

It was roses, roses all the way, and certainly Prince Hal

in the past had had his share of thorns. But the thorns were collecting now at a rapid rate.

In the spring of 1844 Clay accepted a cordial invitation to go to Raleigh, North Carolina. His reception there was tremendous. He was entertained by the Governor and taken next day to the Capitol, where enormous crowds were gathered at a huge barbecue. Warmed with enthusiasm and good southern cooking, they almost crushed the guest of honor in their rush to greet him.

He braced himself against a tree and exclaimed, "Ah! You've treed the old coon at last!"

The future seemed bright indeed; but here at Raleigh, Bob Letcher's fears were realized. The old statesman wrote his famous Raleigh letter, making clear his stand on the annexation of Texas.

The United States had claimed Texas as a part of the Louisiana Purchase in 1803. But in 1819 when the government purchased Florida from Spain, the United States had given up the claim to Texas. As Secretary of State in 1827, Clay had tried unsuccessfully to buy Texas. Someday, he was sure, the United States could acquire it.

For seventeen years after the United States had renounced her claim, Texas had belonged to Mexico. Then under General Sam Houston in 1836 she had become an independent republic—the "Lone Star" republic. And now, at the insistence of colonists from the South and the Southwest, President Tyler had signed a bill of annexation.

Clay did not think annexation "at this present time" was wise for several reasons: Mexico had never acknowledged the independence of Texas; annexation would mean war with Mexico. In the North the people were opposed to annexation because Texas allowed slavery.

As he wrote the Raleigh letter, Clay remembered the days of the Missouri Compromise. He did not want another stormy period like that one. Perhaps he even recalled the days of the War Hawks when he had led the country into war with England. He was older and wiser now. He wished no war. War created more problems than it solved.

War with Mexico, he said, would be an act of aggression. Furthermore, annexation would lead to war. He was against the annexation of Texas. "What the United States needs most are union, peace and patience," he urged.

At the time the Old Prince wrote the letter, annexation was a national issue. The South was clamoring for it. The North was bitterly opposing it.

Clay's enemies were gleeful. They thought his stand would prevent him from getting the nomination. Then Martin Van Buren, the favorite son of the Democratic party, announced that he, too, was against annexation. This act removed annexation as a campaign issue. Was it in the stars, after all, for Henry Clay to win the highest office in the land?

On May 1, 1844, the Whig national convention at Baltimore, Maryland, nominated Clay for the presidency. For his running mate they chose Theodore Frelinghuysen of New Jersey, a faithful Whig and a long-time admirer of the Old Prince.

Feeling ran high. Daniel Webster pledged his support. The Clay supporters were confident of victory. The country celebrated with dinners, banquets and meetings. Clay banners, hats and live coons flooded the country.

Then a month later the Democrats held their convention. Martin Van Buren—the Red Fox—fought a losing battle. His stand on annexation had cost him face in the South and the Southwest. Down at the Hermitage shrewd old Andrew Jackson realized that a successful Democratic candidate must favor annexation. The politicians nominated James K. Polk of Tennessee. Although he had been Speaker of the House of Representatives and Governor of Tennessee, he was not too well known, but—he favored the annexation of Texas. Old Hickory chuckled and wrote to him: "Lash Clay on Texas!"

The campaign became increasingly bitter. The Democrats accused Clay of making a play for the Abolitionist vote. This bewildered and saddened the old statesman, who had always stated clearly his views on Abolition. That was one matter on which he had never compromised.

In the meantime the Abolitionists pulled away from the Whigs and formed their own party. Their candidate was James G. Birney, who was violently opposed to annexing Texas because he feared it would mean the spread of slavery.

Meanwhile Clay persisted in his objections to annexation. He voiced his political creed: "If anyone desires to know the leading and paramount object of my public life, the preservation of this Union will furnish him the key." He felt that annexation might once more bring the United States to the brink of civil war.

Finally November and election time arrived. As usual, due to poor communications, the full returns did not come in for three days. Then they showed that Polk seemed to be ahead. The New York vote would decide the question.

The Clays attended a wedding in Lexington that night. The New York mail would come in at ten o'clock. Several gentlemen went down to the station to get the news. When they came back, one of them silently handed Mr. Clay the paper.

A guest at the party related later that the old man read the message and stood for a moment as if frozen. Then, steeling himself, he picked up a glass of wine, raised it to his lips and smiled.

"I drink to the health and happiness of all assembled here," he said with Spartan simplicity.

With that he resumed his conversation as though nothing had happened. He was sixty-seven. The dream of a lifetime was erased forever. At first the stunned company scarcely realized the blow had struck. Then, one by one, they stole silently away with sorrowful hearts. Harry of the West had fought his last presidential battle.

18

THE OLD WARRIOR

AFTER HIS DEFEAT HENRY CLAY FOUND A SHELTERING REFUGE
at Ashland. Other matters besides public affairs filled his
mind that winter. Financial problems were plaguing him.
In 1839 his taxable property had been listed at one hundred
and forty thousand dollars. Since that time his son Tom
had failed in the hemp business. In going to his aid his
father had given a mortgage on Ashland for twenty thousand. In addition, he had been forced to settle a large estate
which had been left in his hands some years before. By 1844
his taxable property was listed at barely fifty-one thousand.
There was grave danger that he would lose Ashland.

With a heavy heart one morning he made his way to the
Northern Bank, which held his note. As he stood before
the teller's window, a bank employee touched him on the
arm.

"This way, please, Mr. Clay," he requested.

He led the way to the office of the bank president and
stood aside at the door to allow Mr. Clay to enter. The old
man walked across the room and dropped down heavily
into a red plush chair. He shook hands listlessly with Mr.
Tilton, the bank's president, who came across the room to
meet him.

"May I have my note," Henry Clay asked. "I should like
the privilege of renewing it, if it is possible. It was kind of
you to save me the embarrassment of asking for it at the
teller's window, but I am well aware of the extent of my
indebtedness."

Mr. Tilton reached in a drawer of his desk and drew forth an important-looking legal paper.

"Mr. Clay, I am happy to present you with this."

He handed the paper to his visitor, who opened it with trembling hands. For a moment the old man regarded it in a bewildered manner.

"I do not understand—" Henry Clay faltered.

The younger man gave a broad smile. "Somehow word got about that you were in danger of losing Ashland. For days now anonymous contributions have been pouring in from all over the United States. I am happy to tell you that Ashland is again yours—mortgage-free. Furthermore, a sizable balance remains which will be credited to your account."

Clay's faded blue eyes filled with tears. "So it has come to this. I have served my country all my life and end by being an object of charity."

Mr. Tilton shook his head vigorously. "Far from it, sir. This act only proves the love of a grateful people for you."

He went out and closed the door softly behind him. He would leave the Old Prince alone to recover his composure.

The next two years were a period of Indian summer for Henry Clay. If it had not been for the Mexican war cloud on the horizon, it would have been a perfect time. He superintended his crops and watched over his livestock. His wife was at her happiest in the garden and dairy. Tom and James with their families stayed at Ashland while their homes were being built nearby. John had never left home. Henry, Jr., a widower, came over often from Louisville, where he practiced law.

Then in the closing days of President Tyler's administration Texas was admitted into the Union. This brought the United States and Mexico to the verge of war. Although incoming President Polk tried to avert trouble, hostilities commenced in 1846.

Excitement ran high in Lexington. Young men were eager to take part in the fighting. Clay's namesake lost no time in volunteering. He marched away one morning in the Second Regiment of the Kentucky Volunteer Infantry with a score or more of other young men from central Kentucky.

The family at Ashland anxiously followed the progress of the war south of the Rio Grande with maps, newspapers and the old globe with which young Henry had played as a small boy. Due to distance and poor communications, his letters were few and far between. Although the Battle of Buena Vista occurred in February, the news of their son's death in action did not reach the Clays until late March.

To a friend Henry Clay wrote: "It is one of the greatest afflictions which has ever befallen me, in a life which has been full of domestic afflictions. . . . If I could derive any consolation from the fall of my beloved son on the bloody field of Buena Vista, it would be from the fact that, if he were to die, I know he preferred to meet death on the field of battle, in the service of his country."

Soon afterward a painting of young Colonel Clay in uniform appeared on the wall of the dining room at Ashland. He had his mother's lovely, serious eyes. Under the portrait hung the sword he had carried in battle. It had been sent home all the way from Mexico along with a letter of condolence from his commanding officer, General Zachary Taylor.

The war had ended. Mexico had surrendered. The American people were now saying that the Army should march on and take Mexico as well as Texas. Then the United States would round off a major part of the continent.

The question of slavery was still the paramount issue. In Congress, David Wilmot from Pennsylvania had introduced a bill providing that all lands acquired from Mexico be forever free.

The Wilmot Proviso was immediately killed by the southerners. They were determined not only to keep slavery but to extend it.

Henry Clay denounced a proposal to annex Mexico. There was every reason against such an act, he said.

"Does any considerate man believe it possible that two such immense countries, with territories of nearly equal extent, with populations so incongruous—so different in race, in language, in religion, and in laws—could be blended together in one harmonious mass and happily governed by one common authority? Murmurs, discontents, insurrections, rebellion would inevitably ensue, until the incompatible parts would be broken asunder, and possibly, in the frightful struggle, our present glorious Union itself would be dissevered or dissolved," he declared.

Mr. Clay thought—and, as usual, said—that the United States should take no part of Mexico in payment for the expense of war; to add any territory in the face of the quarrel over slavery was unwise.

He finished by saying: "We do positively and emphatically disclaim and disavow any wish or desire on our part to acquire any foreign territory whatever, for the purpose of propagating slavery, or of introducing slaves, from the United States, into such foreign territory."

His speech was received with wild acclaim. Praise poured in from every side. The newspapers carried stories about him. For a short time Henry Clay allowed himself to hope—

Then the Whigs nominated for the presidency General Zachary Taylor, hero of Buena Vista. So much for that! He really had expected nothing more.

Clay spent a pleasant winter in New Orleans racing his horses. Word came to him that he was once more elected to the United States Senate. He was needed again. Congress was in a turmoil over the question of whether the vast territory ceded by Mexico (now California, Nevada, Utah, New Mexico, Arizona and parts of Colorado) should be slave or free.

In November, 1849, he set out for Washington in the splendid red coach that the people of Philadelphia had given him when he was running for the presidency in 1844. The faithful Charles tucked the warm lap robe about the old man's thin legs and clambered up on the driver's seat.

Lucretia, frail and delicate, with a shawl about her stooped old shoulders, tottered out the front door to tell her husband good-by.

"Take good care of him, Charles," she quavered.

"Haven't I always taken good care of him, Miss Lucretia?" Charles asked a little reproachfully.

The coach rolled down the circular driveway. Henry Clay leaned out and waved a long, bony hand. Lucretia watched the vehicle until it disappeared down the turnpike. Then she turned and went slowly back into the house.

On December 3, 1849, the Old Prince was back in the Senate for a memorable session. The South was moving rapidly toward secession. The North was hurrying her along. The subject under debate was slavery.

When the doors of the historic semicircular chamber opened, the old warriors were in their places. In addition to Henry Clay there was Daniel Webster. John Calhoun, now a dying man, was present, but he was not linked with them. He stood solidly with the South. Thomas Hart Benton, Lucretia's cousin and Clay's onetime political enemy, was on the Union side.

There were newcomers, all younger men: William H. Seward, Stephen Douglas, Jefferson Davis. The scepter was passing, but if the younger men were giants, the older ones had been Titans.

Henry Clay was a sad old man. He had foreseen years ago that it would come to this when the Abolitionists first forced their views upon an unwilling South. The fact that California was seeking statehood at the present time may have added fuel to the flames, but it had not kindled the conflagration in the first place.

The Abolitionists had not abated their movements in the least. They had convinced the North that all slaveholders were wicked and cruel. They had persuaded these same northerners to ignore the Constitution and refuse to return runaway slaves to their rightful owners. When Congress opened, the Vermont legislature had presented resolutions to Congress that asked for slavery to be abolished from the District of Columbia.

The South resisted the northern demands with all their might. They even said that the Union had already ended.

These words pierced Henry Clay's heart. He hurried to his rooms at the National Hotel. The time had come to go into action. A solution must be found. He had found one in 1820 and again in 1833; he would find one now even if he was an old man of nearly seventy-three.

He scarcely took time to eat or sleep. Senators, Representatives and other persons of importance came and went up and down the long halls. Clay drove himself until he became ill, but even that did not stop him. One night he went out in a blinding snowstorm to see Daniel Webster. When he left Webster's headquarters, the man from Massachusetts had promised to support him in his plan.

On February 5 Clay was ready to announce what he meant to propose. Still weak from his illness and continuing cough, he had to be assisted up the steps of the Capitol. A vast crowd had gathered in the Senate. The news that he would speak had spread far and wide. It seemed like old times.

Old and feeble but far from broken, Henry Clay rose to his feet and presented his compromise. California, he said, must be admitted as a free state. As for New Mexico, she must be organized as a territory with no mention of slavery. The question would take care of itself, for the climate was not suited to slaves. The boundary line between Texas and New Mexico must be firmly established so there could be no dispute in the future between these states.

He came to the two greatest and final causes for bitterness between the two sections of the country. One was the threat to abolish slavery in the District of Columbia; the other, the refusal on the part of the North to return fugitive slaves to their owners. He felt that the slave trade in the District should be abolished by agreement between North and South.

Then he approved a new Fugitive Slave Law. It was the North's duty to return runaway slaves to their rightful owners. This would be a concession on the part of the North toward the South.

On the other hand, he said, no state had a right to secede. The act could lead only to bloody and exterminating wars. He solemnly pleaded with his countrymen "to pause at the edge of the precipice, before the fearful and disastrous leap is taken in the yawning abyss below, which will inevitably lead to certain and irretrievable destruction . . . and finally, Mr. President, I implore, as the best blessing which Heaven can bestow upon me upon earth, that if the direful and sad event of the dissolution of the Union shall happen, I may not survive to behold the sad and heart-rending spectacle."

Daniel Webster upheld him in a speech that has become, like Clay's, a part of the American heritage. Calhoun opposed them both, but he was so weak that a fellow member had to read his speech for him. When Calhoun died on March 31, the tide seemed to be turning in favor of the Compromise. However, time passed and the fight went on into the summer. Clay was so feeble at times that he seemed at the breaking point, but each day he rallied and took the floor again.

Perhaps his finest hour was when he made his classic utterance:

I know no South, no North, no East, no West to which I owe any allegiance. I owe allegiance to two sovereignties and only two: one is the sovereignty of the Union, and the other is the sovereignty of the State of Kentucky.

Asked about his allegiance if Kentucky seceded, he answered: "If she summons me to the battlefield, or to support her in any cause which is unjust, against the Union, never, *never* will I engage with her in such a cause."

At last in September, 1850, the Compromise Bill passed. The Union was saved once more. And by the man who had sought and been denied the presidency four times!

Weary and ill, Clay returned to Lexington. He was met on the outskirts of the city by a vast crowd of welcoming people, who unhitched his horses and, to the sound of bells and cannon, drew his coach down North Limestone Street and on to the Phoenix Hotel. Did there possibly come to the mind of old Henry Clay the memory of a day when he, as a young lawyer, had won acclaim half a century earlier when he spoke at Maxwell's Grove on a Fourth of July against the infamous Alien and Sedition Acts?

Today, too, he gave them the speech they wanted and then smiled at them in the manner that had endeared him to his public through the years.

"And now," he said in conclusion, "I must ask you to excuse me, for, strange as it may seem, there is an old lady at Ashland whom I would rather see than all of you."

Henry Clay went to Congress for two more terms, growing feebler each time. In June, 1852, he lay dying in Washington. The doctors had wired for his son Thomas to come. His wife was too old and feeble to make the trip. The long years were over. His work was done. On a table beside his bed was a handsome gold medal presented to him by an admiring group from New York. On one side was his head in bas-relief; on the other, a list of his accomplishments:

SENATE, 1806

SPEAKER, 1811

WAR OF 1812 WITH GREAT BRITAIN

GHENT, 1814

SPANISH AMERICA, 1822
AMERICAN SYSTEM, 1824
MISSOURI COMPROMISE, 1821
GREECE, 1824
SECRETARY OF STATE, 1825
PANAMA INSTRUCTIONS, 1826
TARIFF COMPROMISE, 1833
PUBLIC DOMAIN, 1833-1841
PEACE WITH FRANCE PRESERVED, 1835
COMPROMISE, 1850

On the morning of June 29, 1852, Henry Clay came to the end of his life and his service to his country. The two had gone hand in hand.

They brought him home to Kentucky and let him lie in state at Ashland until he was borne to his grave. The account of his funeral procession is legend in the Bluegrass. It stretched from Ashland east of the town to the cemetery on the western outskirts. The little town of ten thousand could hardly contain the throngs that came from far and near to do him honor. At sunset on July 10 he was laid to rest with a salute of thirty-one guns—one for each state then in the Union.

The long battle over, he sleeps today on a rolling, grassy, sunlit knoll in the Lexington Cemetery, where the youth of his generation had picnicked at Boswell's Grove. Over his sarcophagus a grateful people have erected a granite tomb that towers over the surrounding countryside even as the character of the man towers over the characters of his lesser fellow beings.

On a tablet in the crypt are carved the words that best explain his life's progress and purpose:

I KNOW NO SOUTH, NO NORTH, NO EAST, NO WEST.

BIBLIOGRAPHY

Adams, John Quincy. *The Diary of John Quincy Adams, 1794–1845.* Longmans, Green & Co., New York, 1928.

Bradford, Gamaliel. *As God Made Them.* Houghton, Mifflin Co., Boston, 1929.

Clay, Henry. *The Papers of Henry Clay,* Vol. 1, *The Rising Statesman.* Edited by James F. Hopkins and Mary W. M. Hargreaves. University of Kentucky Press, 1959.

Clay, Thomas Hart. *Henry Clay.* G. W. Jacobs & Co., Philadelphia, 1910.

Colman Edna M. *Seventy-five Years of White House Gossip.* Doubleday, Page & Co. New York, 1925.

Eaton, Clement. *Henry Clay and the Art of American Politics.* Little, Brown. Boston, 1957.

Gallatin, James. *The Diary of James Gallatin.* Charles Scribner's Sons. New York, 1916.

Hunt, Gaillard. *Life in America One Hundred Years Ago.* Harper & Brothers. New York, 1914.

Mayo, Bernard. *Henry Clay: Spokesman of the West,* Vol. 1. Houghton Mifflin. Boston, 1937.

Mayo, Barbara. *Henry Clay.* Farrar & Rinehart. New York, 1943.

Smith, Margaret Bayard. *The First Forty Years of Washington Society.* Charles Scribner's Sons. New York, 1906.

Van Deusen, Glyndon G. *The Life of Henry Clay.* Little, Brown & Co. Boston, 1937.

Whiteley, Emily Stone. "Between the Acts at Ghent." *Virginia Quarterly Review,* Vol. V, January, 1929.

INDEX

About the Author

KATHARINE E. WILKIE was born in Lexington, Kentucky, received her education in Fayette County schools and at the University of Kentucky where her writing career began. She teaches eighth grade at Lafayette Junior High School in Lexington, and combines that career with writing biography for children and teen-agers.